D1484040

THE DIMER ACIDS

The chemical and physical properties, reactions, and applications of polymer-ized fatty acids.

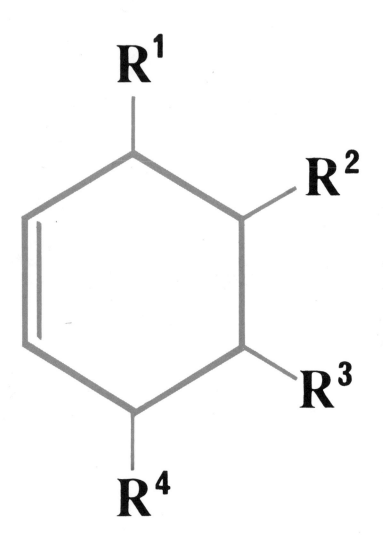

THE DIMER ACIDS

The chemical and physical properties, reactions, and applications of polymerized fatty acids.

Edited by

Edward C. Leonard

Chemical

Memphis, Tennessee 38101
Operation of
Kraftco Corporation

Library of Congress Catalog Card Number: 75-3895

Leonard, Edward C.
   The Dimer Acids.
Connecticut   Humko Sheffield Chemical
April 1975

2-5-75

PREFACE

Polymerized fatty acids, called dimer acids, are now an important internationally-marketed specialty chemical. Dimer acids, in various forms, have wide application, particularly as feedstock for polyamide resin manufacture. The polyamides, in their turn, are the base for adhesives, inks, and coatings.

This monograph, which is the result of a suggestion of S L Kopald, Jr., President of Humko Sheffield Chemical, is the first comprehensive treatment of the properties, reactions, and applications of dimer acids. The purpose of the book is, first, to describe what dimer acids *are:* physically, chemically, and structurally; and, second, to describe what dimer acids *do:* i.e., to outline the commercial applications of the products. The book does not cover, in depth, the manufacture of the product, which is described superficially in the patent literature, and in great detail in proprietary intracompany reports.

This book has been written by five scientists employed by Kraftco Corporation. These are:

Lawrence U. Berman,
born in Chicago, Illinois in 1919,
received his Master's Degree in Organic Chemistry from
    Northwestern University, Evanston, Illinois,
is now Research Chemist with Kraftco Research and Development.

Lawrence A. Fury,
born in Chicago, Illinois in 1938,
received his PhD in Organic Chemistry from Vanderbilt
    University, Nashville, Tennessee,
is now Manager of Marketing Research, Humko Sheffield
    Chemical.

Edward Charles Leonard,
born in Burlington, North Carolina in 1927,
received his PhD in Organic Chemistry from the University of North Carolina
    and his Master's in Business Administration from the
    University of Chicago,
is now Technical Director, Humko Sheffield Chemical.

Melvin L. Loeb,
born in New York City, New York in 1943,
received his PhD in Organic Chemistry from Massa-

chusetts Institute of Technology, Cambridge, Massachusetts,
is now Group Leader with Kraftco Research and Development.

Kenneth T. Mecklenborg,
born in Cincinnati, Ohio in 1927,
received his PhD in Organic Chemistry from the Applied Science Laboratory of the University of Cincinnati, Cincinnati, Ohio,
is now Manager of Applications with Humko Sheffield Chemical.

We also acknowledge the editorial assistance of Dr. F. X. Markley, Manager, Industrial Chemical Products Laboratory, Kraftco Research and Development, and the contributions to Chapter 5 of J. P. Duffy, Manager, Customer Service, Humko Chemical.

We are grateful for the stenographic contributions of Mina Elliot, Heather Madsen, Barbara Vance, Linda Ware, and Dorothy Zessack.

Industries based on dimer acids and their proliferation products are the result of the work and skill of hundreds of men and women—operators, technicians, marketing experts, and other businesspeople. The chemical industry has every reason to be grateful to them.

Memphis, Tennessee   E. C. Leonard
November, 1974

CONTENTS

The General Characteristics of Dimer Acids

Lawrence U. Berman and Melvin L. Loeb—Research and Development, Kraftco Corporation, Glenview, Illinois

A. INTRODUCTION

One of the reactions common to all unsaturated, straight-chain aliphatic acids and their alkyl esters is self-condensation to form high-molecular-weight dibasic and polybasic acids. Under the proper conditions (clay-catalyzed, thermal dimerization in commercial practice), one molecule of an unsaturated fatty acid will react with another to form a dicarboxylic acid with double the original molecular weight. Even after stripping to remove most of the low-molecular-weight ($\sim C_{18}$) fraction, the resulting commercial product is not a single entity, but is a collection of isomers grouped together under the designation "dimer acids".

Commercially, then, dimer acids are mixtures of 36-carbon dibasic acids, smaller amounts of 54-carbon tribasic acids, still higher-molecular-weight polybasic acids, and trace levels of so-called "monomer". "Monomer" is a mixture of the unchanged saturated and unsaturated fatty acids in the feedstock, together with unpolymerized but structurally-modified monobasic unsaturated fatty acids. Other commercial variations of the basic "dimer" product are distilled dimer acids, in which the C_{36} moiety is separated by distillation from higher- and lower-molecular-weight materials; hydrogenated dimer acids; and "trimer", in which the 54-carbon atom entity constitutes a majority of the material. In addition, "monomer", the aforementioned non-polymerized, monobasic reaction by-product, has significant commercial application.

The polymerized fatty acids have certain properties which result from a unique combination of molecular, physical, and chemical characteristics. These include di-, or higher, functionality with respect to carboxyl groups, high molecular weight, olefinic unsaturation, and room-temperature liquidity. It is these characteristics that have lent themselves to the production of commercially-important derivatives, principally the polyamide resins.

These polyamide resin derivatives can be utilized by themselves or can be employed as intermediates for the manufacture of other products. The principal end-uses of these plastics are in hot-melt adhesives, printing inks, curing agents for epoxy resins, and surface coatings such as paints. A myriad of other, but considerably lower-volume, uses for dimer acids lie in a number of diverse areas. These include polyester resins, lube-oil additives, and corrosion inhibitors.

Twenty five years ago dimer acids were a laboratory curiosity, characterized experimentally by workers at the Northern Regional Research Laboratory of the Agricultural Research Service of the United States Department of Agriculture. In 1974 there were three major producers of dimer acids. These were Humko Sheffield Chemical, an operation of Kraftco Corporation; Emery Industries, Inc.; and General Mills Chemicals, Inc. The dimer acids plants for these three companies were located, respectively, in Memphis, Tennessee; Cincinnati, Ohio; and Kankakee, Illinois.

There were also, in the early 1970's, three smaller dimer acids manufacturers listed in one reference (1): AZS Corporation, AZ Products, Inc., Division; Crosby Chemicals, Inc.; and Union Camp Corporation, Harchem Division. Whether or not all three were still manufacturing the product in 1974 is not known.

Plant production capacities of the three principal manufacturers of dimer acids is not published information. Since the production of the dimer-based polyamide resins *is* public information, some inferential estimation of U.S. dimer production can be made. Table 1 (2) shows United States current and future consumption, actual and estimated, of the resins.

TABLE 1

United States Consumption—Dimer-Based Polyamide Resins

Year	Millions of Pounds
1972	32
1974 E	36
1978 E	45
E = Estimated	

The combined dimer acids content of the resins will vary, depending on the type of end-product, but an average of 80% dimer acids content is probably a useful number. Thus, it is inferred that, in this major end-use alone, 20 million to 30 million pounds of polymerized fatty acids are being consumed annually in the United States.

B. DIMER ACIDS MANUFACTURE AND FEEDSTOCK

In present-day commercial practice, dimer acids are prepared by the thermal condensation of unsaturated fatty acids, usually catalyzed by small amounts of montmorillonite clay. These manufacturing procedures are described in a number of United States patents assigned to Kraftco Corporation, to Emery Industries, and to General Mills (3-11). These patents and a series of papers by den Otter (12) detail the effect of reaction temperatures, pressures, clay content and type, and other reaction variables. Another, and overwhelmingly important, variable is the unsaturated fatty acid used as feedstock for dimer production. The published literature describes the use of starting materials (both free fatty acids and alkyl esters) which are rich in polyunsaturates such as those derived from drying and semi-drying vegetable and marine oils—linoleic and linolenic acid and their higher-molecular-weight homologues. The literature also describes the use of monounsaturated fatty acids such as oleic acid and its isomers, erucic acid, undecylenic acid, and other monounsaturated fatty acids.

The principal feedstock for production of dimer acids, from the outset of commercial production, has been tall oil fatty acids, the cheapest unsaturated fatty acid available. This raw material is produced by the high-vacuum fractionation of tall oil, which is the generic name for the products derived from the black liquor residue of the kraft pulping process.

A typical analysis of commercial-grade tall oil fatty acids is shown in Table 2.

TABLE 2

Typical Tall Oil Fatty Acids Analysis (13)

Color, Gardner 1963	3
Acid value	196.0
Saponification value	198.0
Iodine value	128.0
Unsaponifiables, %	1.0
Rosin acids, %	1.0
Moisture, %	0.09
Ash, %	0.0003
Total fatty acid, %	98.0
Fatty acid composition, %	
palmitic	0.5
stearic	2.0
oleic	51.0
linoleic	37.0
$C_{18:2}$ *cis-trans*	3.0
$C_{18:2}$ *trans-trans*	3.0
unknown	1.5

Dimer acids are, for the most part, a variety of substituted cyclohexenedicarboxylic acids formed by a Diels-Alder-type reaction. The multiplicity of geometric, structural (positional), and conformational isomers results in a complex, difficult-to-separate mixture. Dimer acids structure can be simplistically represented as follows:

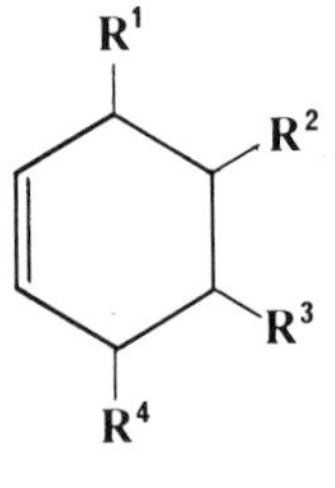

If head-to-head condensation has occurred, the adjacent R groups (e.g., R^1 and R^2 or R^3 and R^4) will be terminated in carboxyl groups while the other two adjacent groups will be hydrocarbon terminated. If head-to-tail condensation has occurred, the R groups will alternate in terminating carboxyl and hydrocarbon groups. The carboxy-terminating groups can have structures such as:

$-(CH_2)_8COOH$, $-CH=CH(CH_2)_8COOH$, $-(CH_2)_7COOH$, $-CH_2CH=CH(CH_2)_7COOH$, $-CH=CH(CH_2)_7COOH$, etc., and the hydrocarbon-terminating group can be represented by:

$CH_3(CH_2)_4-$, $CH_3(CH_2)_5-$, $CH_3(CH_2)_7-$,
$CH_3(CH_2)_4CH=CH-$, $CH_3(CH_2)_4CH=CHCH_2-$, etc.

Many additional isomers are formed during the dimerization reaction; these will be discussed in subsequent sections.

C. BY-PRODUCTS OF THE DIMERIZATION REACTION

In the commercial manufacture of dimer acids, two by-products are formed in addition to the major product. These are "monomer acids" and "trimer acids".

1. *Monomer Acids*

Monomer acids consist of a series of compounds which include not only unreacted starting material, but, also, any other monobasic acids which have a molecular weight roughly equivalent to that of the starting fatty acids. During commercial processing, monomer acids are separated from the polymerized fatty acids by fractionation or molecular distillation. Analysis of monomer acids shows that some of the fatty acids present in the starting material have been altered—both in terms of degree of unsaturation and with respect to the skeletal structure of the carbon chain. Therefore, in addition to the unreacted unsaturated and saturated fatty acids carried over from the starting material, there are also present larger amounts of stearic and palmitic acids than are found in the feedstock, and material *not* found in the feedstock, i.e., structurally-modified acids called "iso acids".

"Iso acids" are branched-chain acids of molecular weight equivalent to the parent acid for which the iso acid is named. As an example, isostearic acid would be any (or more than one) of the non-linear saturated C_{18} carboxylic acids. Although the mechanism of rearrangement has not been proved conclusively, formation of these modified acids seems to be the result of the presence of clay. There is also evidence for the formation of iso acids at much higher temperatures in the absence of clay (14).

The monomer acids removed from the dimerization reaction mixture show a fairly high degree of unsaturation. If these acids are subjected to dimerization conditions, however, they can be polymerized only to a small extent (15). If monomer acids are hydrogenated, the stearic acid content of the product increases (16). Since the amount of polyunsaturated fatty acids in the unhydrogenated monomer acids is negligible, it has been concluded that monomer acids contain isomeric straight-chain, monounsaturated C_{18} fatty acids.

McMahon and Crowell have indicated that monomer acids from tall oil fatty acids consist of stearic, octadecenoic, and branched acids, both saturated and unsaturated (16). They concluded that the branched acids contain an average of 1.3 branched methyl groups/acid molecule with the branching occurring at mid-chain. The octadecenoic acid is present as both the *cis* and *trans* isomers with the *trans* isomer predominating.

Both the modified- and straight-chain unsaturated acids in monomer acids can be catalytically hydrogenated relatively easily to a very low level of unsaturation (14). The resulting saturated iso acids are liquid, with a solidification point (titer) substantially below room temperature. They can be separated from straight-chain solid acids by low-temperature solvent crystallization (14). The iso acids obtained from this process have a titer of <10°C and are commercially available (17). They show oxidation stability characteristics superior to other liquid (unsaturated) fatty acids.

Table 9 in Chapter 2 shows the properties of Century 1105, an isostearic acid marketed by Union Camp Corporation (18).

2. *Trimer Acids*

The dimerization reaction also produces a substantial quantity (~10%) of material having a molecular weight approximately three times that of the starting fatty acid. These tribasic acids are called trimer acids. They may be the result of a Diels-Alder-type condensation of a molecule of dimer acid with a molecule of monomeric unsaturated fatty acid. Other oligomers (tetramers and pentamers) can also be detected in the reaction mixture, but in small amounts.

Functionally defined, trimer acids is the material present in the residue after dimer acids are removed by molecular distillation. Typical properties of commercial trimer acids are listed in Table 7 in Chapter 2.

The amount of trimer acids present in a dimerization reaction mixture depends on a number of factors, including:

1) the oleic/linoleic acid ratio in the raw material,
2) the type of clay used in dimerization, and
3) the reaction conditions used.

Little work has been reported on the structure of trimer acids and little interest in general has been shown in the chemistry of this class of compounds.

REFERENCES FOR CHAPTER ONE

1. *Chemical Economics Handbook,* Stanford Research Institute, Menlo Park, California, March 1974, p. 580.1032S.
2. *Chemical Economics Handbook,* Stanford Research Institute, Menlo Park, California, March 1974, p. 580.1031H.
3. C. G. Goebel, U.S. Patent 2,482,761 (1949); 3,100,784 (1963).
4. F. O. Barrett, C. G. Goebel and R. M. Peters, U.S. Patent 2,793,219 (1957); 2,793,220 (1957).
5. L. D. Myers, C. G. Goebel and F. O. Barrett, U.S. Patent 2,955,121 (1960); 3,076,003 (1963).
6. E. M. Fischer, U.S. Patent 3,157,681 (1964).
7. S. E. Miller, U.S. Patent 3,412,039 (1968).
8. J. E. Milks and N. H. Conroy, U.S. Patent 3,422,124 (1969).
9. N. H. Conroy, U.S. Patent 3,632,822 (1972).
10. L. U. Berman, U.S. Patent 3,732,263 (1973).
11. *Chemical Economics Handbook,* Stanford Research Institute, Menlo Park, California, March 1974, pp. 580.1031A *ff.*
12. M. J. A. M. den Otter, *Fette, Seifen, Anstrichm.,* **72,** 667 (1970); *ibid.,* **72,** 875 (1970); *ibid.,* **72,** 1056 (1970).
13. The properties listed in Table 2 are a composite rather than those of a specific commercial product.
14. R. M. Peters, U.S. Patent 2,812,342 (1957).
15. An attempt to improve overall conversion by redimerization of the monomer acids is reported by N. H. Conroy, U.S. Patent 3,632,822 (1972).
16. D. H. McMahon and E. P. Crowell, *J. Amer. Oil Chem. Soc.,* **51,** 522 (1974).
17. These products are manufactured and marketed by Emery Industries, Inc. and Union Camp Corporation.
18. Used by permission.

SUPPLEMENTARY REFERENCES

Klare S. Markley, Ed., *Fatty Acids,* Part 2, Interscience Publishers, Inc., New York, 1961, pp. 1036 *ff.*

Herman F. Mark and Norman G. Gaylord, Eds., *Encyclopedia of Polymer Science and Technology,* Vol. 10, Interscience Publishers, Inc., New York, 1969, pp. 599 *ff.*

Raymond E. Kirk and Donald F. Othmer, Eds., *Encyclopedia of Chemical Technology,* 2nd Ed., Vol. 8, Interscience Publishers, Inc., 1965, pp. 847 *ff.*

M. Morimoto, M. Saito and A. Goukon, U.S. Patent 3,773,806 (1973).

G. Dieckelmann and H. Rutzen, U.S. Patent 3,507,890 (1970).

D. H. Wheeler, U.S. Patent 3,444,220 (1969).

H. G. Arlt, Jr., U.S. Patent 3,367,952 (1968).

J. W. Breakey, G. A. Silverstone and R. Rowe, *J. Amer. Oil Chem. Soc.*, **44,** 191 (1967); British Patent 1,048,315 (1966).

H. W. G. Heynen, W. H. M. J. Van Optal and M. J. A. M. den Otter, *Fette, Seifen, Anstrichm.*, **74,** 677 (1972).

A. N. Sagredos, *Fette, Seifen, Anstrichm.*, **76,** 8 (1974).

A. N. Sagredos and J. D. von Mikusch, *Tetrahedron*, **26,** 5587 (1970).

A. Hase, O. Harva and T. Pakkanen, *J. Amer. Oil Chem. Soc.*, **51,** 181 (1974).

S. Dev and U. R. Nayak, U.S. Patent 3,488,366 (1970).

D. E. A. Rivett, *J. Amer. Oil Chem. Soc.*, **33,** 635 (1956).

J. A. MacDonald, *J. Amer. Oil Chem. Soc.*, **33,** 394 (1956).

T. N. Mehta and S. A. Sharma, *J. Amer. Oil Chem. Soc.*, **33,** 38, (1956).

R. F. Paschke and D. H. Wheeler, *J. Amer. Oil Chem. Soc.*, **32,** 473 (1955).

Structure and Properties of Dimer Acids

2

Lawrence U. Berman and Melvin L. Loeb—Research and
Development, Kraftco Corporation, Glenview, Illinois

A. STRUCTURE OF DIMER ACIDS

Only the thermal and clay-catalyzed/thermal processes for
dimer acids manufacture have had commercial significance.
This discussion, therefore, is confined to the dimer acids from
those processes. Other methods have been reviewed by Figge
(1), Guillaumin (2), Cowan (3) and Byrne (4). These include
oxidative, cationic and free-radical dimerizations.

Historically, interest in dimer acids was stimulated by work
on the "heat bodying" (thermal polymerization) of drying oils.
Two patents (5) issued to De Nordiske Fabriker in 1919 described the preparation of polymeric fatty acids by heating
unsaturated alkali soaps under steam pressure. Apparently,
these products were not suited to commercial application at
that time.

In 1929, Scheiber (6) stated that the conjugation of isolated
double bonds was a prerequisite for heat polymerization of
oils. Kappelmeier (7) extended this thinking to postulate a
Diels-Alder-type reaction between conjugated and non-
conjugated fatty acids. These hypotheses were supported by
Bradley and co-workers (8), who confirmed polymerization as
the principal thermal reaction of polyunsaturated esters and
who also isolated a monocyclic and a bicyclic dimer from
methyl linoleate to which they tentatively assigned the following structures (or isomers thereof):

$$CH=CH(CH_2)_7COOCH_3$$

$$|$$

$$CH$$

$$CH_3(CH_2)_5CH \qquad CH(CH_2)_7COOCH_3$$

$$CH_3(CH_2)_5CH \qquad CH$$

$$CH$$

and

$$CH_3(CH_2)_3CH=CHCH$$

(A structural diagram showing the cyclic dimer structure with the following labeled groups: $(CH_2)_7COOCH_3$, CH, CH, $CH(CH_2)_7COOCH_3$, C, CH_2, $CH_3(CH_2)_3CH=CHCH$, CH, $CH_3(CH_2)_3CH$, CH, CH)

A proof of the cyclic structure of thermal dimerization products was furnished by Waterman and associates (9). They converted dimer esters to alcohols by a Grignard reaction, followed by dehydration and subsequent hydrogenation to the hydrocarbons. The cyclic character of the hydrocarbon products was shown by molecular refraction studies. Wheeler (10) showed the effect of geometric isomerization on the "relative speed" of polymerization (Table 3). This work supports the Scheiber-Kappelmeier hypothesis.

TABLE 3

Relative Thermal Polymerization Rates
of Dienoic and Trienoic C_{18} Methyl Esters

Compound	Conjugation	cis-, trans- configuration	Relative speed
9, 12-Linoleate	No	cis, trans	0.74
9, 12-Linoleate	No	cis, cis	1.0
9, 12-Linoleate	No	trans, trans	1.2
9, 12, 15-Linolenate	No	cis, cis, cis	2.4
9, 11- and 10, 12-Linoleate	Yes	cis, trans	5.8
10, 12-Linoleate	Yes	trans, trans	26.0
9, 11, 13-α-Eleostearate	Yes	cis, trans, trans	170.0
9, 11, 13-β-Eleostearate	Yes	trans, trans, trans	340.0

Clingman and co-workers (11) established the presence of a 1,2,3,4-tetrasubstituted six-membered ring (which confirms a Diels-Alder-type dimerization) in the product of the dimerization of methyl β-eleostearate by aromatization of the product and oxidation to benzene-1,2,3,4-tetracarboxylic acid. Similar conclusions were reached by Kapadi and Nayak (12) on the basis of mass spectral and chemical data.

Paschke and Wheeler (13) obtained four structural (positional) isomers from dimerizing conjugated (10-*trans*-,12-*trans*-)methyl linoleate and elucidated the structures on the basis of chemical and spectral data. All of the isomers were tetrasubstituted cyclohexenes with one olefinic double bond in the side chain. The chains were randomly oriented, depending on whether "head-to-head" or "head-to-tail" condensation occurred and also on whether the 10- or the 12-double bond was the dienophile. The possible structures were as shown in Figure 1 (**1A** and **1B** are "head-to-head" and **2A** and **2B** are "head-to-tail").

Sen Gupta and Scharmann (14) obtained similar results using the 9-*trans*-,11-*trans*-linoleate. They separated the different dimers by thin layer chromatography and determined the respective structures by mass spectrometry. Neither group of investigators was able to distinguish the geometric *(cis-, trans-)* isomers.

Wheeler and his associates (15) isolated bicyclic and tricyclic dimers, in addition to the monocyclic cyclohexene dimers, from the thermal dimerization of "normal" (9-*cis*-,12-*cis*-)-methyl linoleate. These results were disputed by Sen Gupta (16a) who was unable to find any tetrasubstituted cyclohexenes, but isolated instead bicyclic, tricyclic, and polycyclic compounds under essentially the same reaction conditions. In later work (16b), however, he did find evidence for a small amount of the expected monocyclic dimers.

Finally, Wheeler and his co-workers (17a) reacted the normal 9-*cis*-,12-*cis*- acid in the presence of a catalytic amount of clay, and found that the ratio of monocyclic to bicyclic dimer in the product was much higher than in material prepared by thermal methods. Tricyclic compounds also were found to be relatively minor in the case of the clay-catalyzed product. In addition to the expected tetrasubstituted cyclohexene, the product contained compounds with an aromatic ring having both saturated and unsaturated side chains. They suggested a sequence of reactions: first, clay-catalyzed double bond conjugation; second, a Diels-Alder reaction; and, finally, a clay-catalyzed hydrogen transfer leading to dehydrogenation of the cyclohexene ring. This work has been largely confirmed in a recent study by McMahon and Crowell (17b). However, compared to the results of Wheeler, these workers have found a much larger polycyclic component in the dimer acids derived from linoleic acid. With tall oil fatty acids, the proportion of polycyclic structures was lower and, in addi-

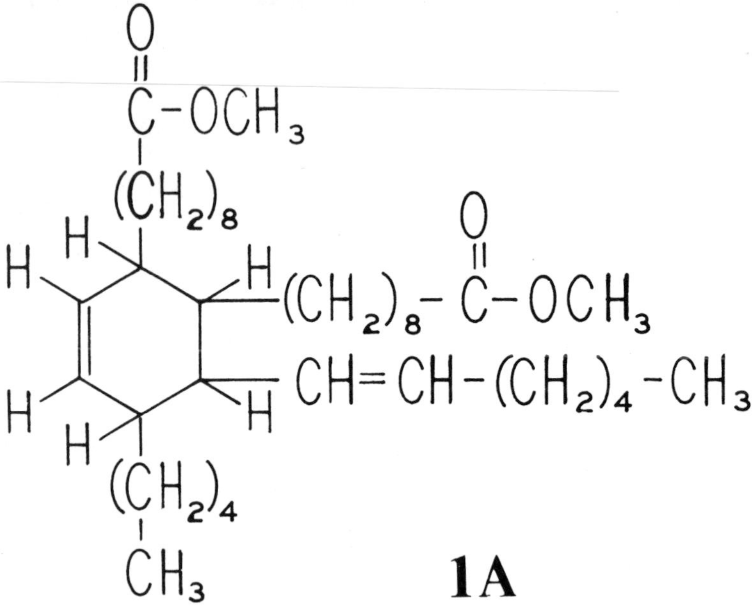

$$\underset{\displaystyle \overset{\displaystyle O}{\|}}{C}-OCH_3$$

$(CH_2)_8$

$(CH_2)_8-\overset{\displaystyle O}{\overset{\displaystyle \|}{C}}-OCH_3$

$CH=CH-(CH_2)_4-CH_3$

$(CH_2)_4$

CH_3

1A

$$\underset{\displaystyle \overset{\displaystyle O}{\|}}{C}-OCH_3$$

$(CH_2)_8$

$CH=CH-(CH_2)_4-CH_3$

$(CH_2)_8-\overset{\displaystyle C}{\underset{\displaystyle O}{\|}}-OCH_3$

$(CH_2)_4$

CH_3

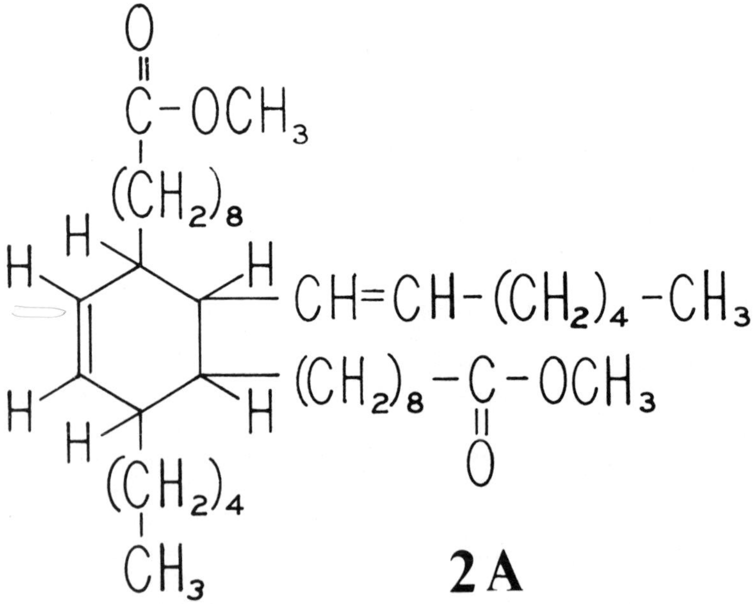

2A

Figure 1. Possible skeletal structures of dimers.

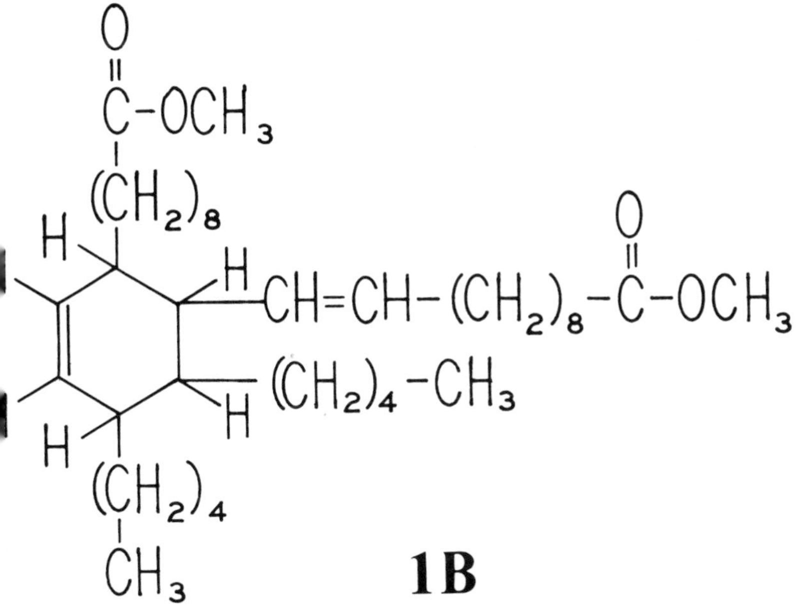

1B

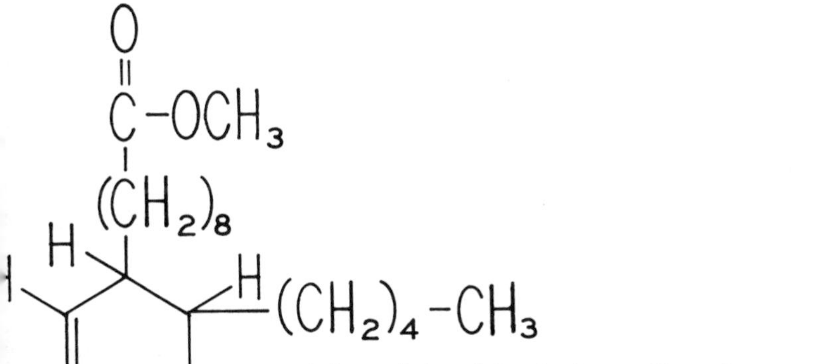

2B

Figure 1.   (continued)

tion, a significant proportion of linear structures was found (based on uncalibrated mass spectral data).

In considering the structures of dimer acids, a simplistic approach is to examine the possibilities of products from linoleic acid. If, for example, that acid were conjugated in the 10-*trans*-, 12-*trans*- positions, the structural isomers shown in Figure 2 would be possible.

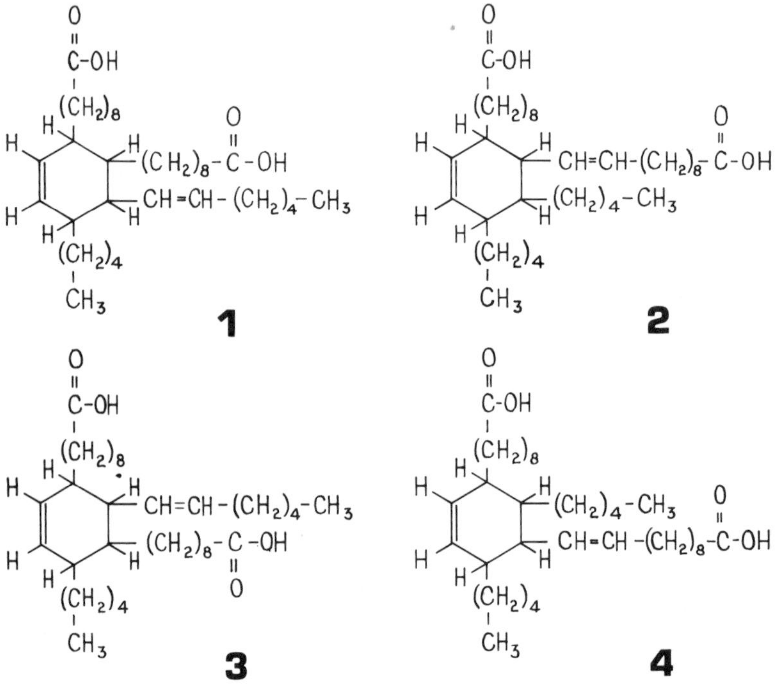

Figure 2. Possible skeletal structures of dimers (10-*trans*-,12-*trans*-).

Each of the four structural isomers has sixteen *cis*-, *trans*-isomeric possibilities, giving a total of 64 isomers. In addition, several aromatic analogues, with both saturated and unsaturated side chains, are possible.

If linoleic acid becomes conjugated in the 9-*trans*-, 11-*trans*-positions, four different structural isomers can result. These also can have geometric variations and aromatic analogues.

It has also been shown (18) that, under the influence of clay, the double bonds shift position in the carbon chain. Thus, many additional compounds are possible from the multiplicity of Diels-Alder-type condensation products.

As discussed earlier, bicyclic dimer products are also possible. The "head-to-head" bicyclic dimer that could be formed from the 10-*trans*-,12-*trans*-linoleic acid is illustrated in Figure 3.

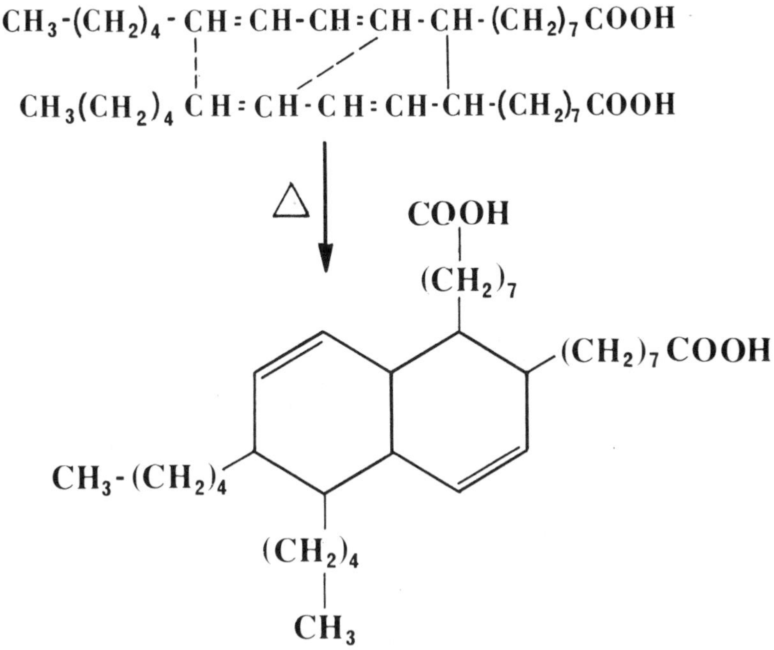

$$CH_3\text{-}(CH_2)_4\text{-}CH\!:\!CH\text{-}CH\!:\!CH\text{-}CH\text{-}(CH_2)_7\,COOH$$

$$CH_3(CH_2)_4\;CH\!:\!CH\text{-}CH\!:\!CH\text{-}CH\text{-}(CH_2)_7\,COOH$$

Figure 3. Intramolecular cyclization of a 10-*trans*-, 12-*trans*-dimer.

Commercial fatty acids rich in polyunsaturates contain oleic acid as well, in varying amounts which depend on the source. Oleic acid can act as a dienophile in the dimerization reaction and thus enter into a Diels-Alder-type reaction with linoleic acid. Here again, "head-to-head" and "head-to-tail" structural isomers can be formed as a result of reaction with the conjugated forms of linoleic acid. These structural isomers, all with saturated side chains, and the concomitant geometric forms, would theoretically yield many additional isomers.

Additionally, oleic acid can polymerize by itself. The methyl ester of oleic acid was thermally polymerized (in the absence of clay) by Sen Gupta (19). The principal component of the dimer mixture was shown to be:

$$CH_3(CH_2)_8CH(CH_2)_7COOCH_3$$
$$CH_3(CH_2)_7CH\!=\!C(CH_2)_7COOCH_3$$

In addition, monoenoic, dienoic, and saturated ring structures were found, with the structures proposed for the latter as follows:

$$CH_3(CH_2)_6CH—CHCH_2(CH_2)_7COOCH_3$$
$$CH_3(CH_2)_7CH—CH(CH_2)_7COOCH_3$$

and

$$CH_3(CH_2)_6CH \overset{CH_2}{\diagdown} CH(CH_2)_7COOCH_3$$
$$CH_3(CH_2)_7CH——CH(CH_2)_7COOCH_3$$

Utilizing clay catalysis, oleic acid was dimerized by den Otter (20). His "results indicate that a fairly large amount of saturated fatty acids is formed, most likely by hydrogen transfer. According to this assumption, dienoic acids must also be formed, which are readily dimerized to cyclic dimers. Thus the common assumption that the dimers of oleic acid obtained by this process are non-cyclic, becomes improbable" (20b). The cyclic nature of the product was confirmed by the previously-discussed method of Waterman (9). However, McMahon and Crowell have shown that dimer acids from oleic and elaidic acids contain a higher percentage of linear components, about 40%, than that obtained from either linoleic or tall oil fatty acids (17b).

The foregoing discussion has covered some of the complexities involved in the characterization of dimer acids. Only a few of the possible isomers have been characterized. It seems probable that the use of modern analytical tools will slowly add to the body of knowledge of dimer acids. As this knowledge becomes more sophisticated, the relationship of reaction conditions and type of feedstock, on the one hand, and dimer and end-product properties, on the other, will become considerably clearer to both the producers and the users.

B. ANALYSIS OF DIMER ACIDS

Standardized procedures are used to measure some of the properties of dimer acids. Examples are listed in Table 4 (AOCS methods refer to American Oil Chemists' Society, *Official and Tentative Methods*, Part 2, 3rd Ed., 1973. ASTM methods refer to American Society for Testing and Materials, published in various years).

TABLE 4

Physical Property Characterization of Dimer Acids

Property	Method
Acid value	AOCS Te 1a-64
Saponification value	AOCS Tl 1a-64
Unsaponifiables, %	AOCS Tk 1a-64
Flash and fire points	ASTM D92-72
Gardner color	ASTM D1544-63T
Viscosity { kinematic	ASTM D445-65
Viscosity { Gardner-Holdt	(21)
Specific gravity	AOCS To 1a-64
Pour point	ASTM D97-66

The determination of iodine value (IV) is merely an approximation of unsaturation, because tertiary allylic hydrogens in the compounds are capable of substitution by halogen atoms. Cowan and his co-workers (22) showed that the amount of excess iodine monochloride reagent added, in a Wijs procedure, had a pronounced effect on the IV. They found that the 4-hr Kaufmann procedure (23), however, showed no IV variation, for a given sample, with the amount of excess reagent (alcoholic bromine).

Variations in digestion times for the dimer acids also give variations in the iodine value. Most laboratories, as a time-saving device, use the standard Wijs procedure, with either a 30-minute (24) or a 60-minute (25) digestion time.

Currently, there is no accepted, standardized method for the direct determination of monomer, dimer, and trimer acids. Firestone (26) suggested urea adduction (of the methyl esters) as a means of determining monomer in distilled dimer. The method is tedious, however, and the non-adducting, branched-chain monomer is recovered with the polymeric fraction. Firestone (27) also developed a micro sublimination procedure as an improvement on urea adduction for estimation of the polymer fraction. Incomplete removal of monomer esters, or loss of dimer during distillation, can lead to error.

Thin-layer chromatography (TLC) (14, 28) has been suggested for the estimation of amounts of the various methyl esters. Although the limits of detection are reported to be very low (*ca.* 0.005-0.01%), the precision is not good (*ca.* 5-10%). Furthermore, the procedure is tedious. Paper chromatographic methods have the same disadvantages (28a, 29).

In work with methyl esters from dimerized soya and linseed oils, Cowan and his associates (22, 30) used a short-path alembic still to strip off the monomer, then distilled the polymer fractions using a forerunner of the modern thin-film molecular still (31). Bradley and Johnson (32) used a molecular still for the bulk fractionation of the reaction product from thermally-dimerized methyl linoleate. Harrison and Wheeler (33) used a centrifugal molecular still for fractionation of dimer and trimer acids from dimerizate from which monomer had previously been removed. Micro stills (34, 35) have been devised for measurement of levels of monomer, dimer, and trimer acids (after conversion to the corresponding methyl esters). The most elegant of the micromolecular stills has been described by Paschke and his co-workers (36). The methyl esters were dispersed on a bale of glass wool to minimize thermal decomposition. The bale was surrounded by a thermostatically-controlled heating block and suspended from a quartz helix. The extension of the helix was proportional to the weight loss from the bale and was measured with a cathetometer. Descriptions and diagrams of the various molecular stills, as well as other methods of analysis available through 1962, were reviewed by Firestone (28b).

Various column chromatographic methods have been proposed for the analysis of dimer acids. Frankel and Evans (37) used liquid partition (elution) chromatography on silicic acid columns to determine monomeric, dimeric, and trimeric acids as the methyl esters or as the free acids. Greaves and Laker (38) used gas-liquid chromatography (GLC) on the methyl esters for the determination of monomer acids. Although their technique did not indicate the amount of polymer, it was used to follow the course of polymerization by measuring the disappearance of 18-carbon unsaturated fatty acids. Hase (39) reported a GLC method for determination of monomer and dimer acids, as the methyl esters. Paylor, et al. (40) also used a GLC method for the analysis of both monomer and dimer acids.

A relatively new technique, gel-permeation chromatography (GPC), has come into use for the quantitative analysis of dimer acids. Chang (41) was able to determine small amounts of fatty acid dimers and resin acid dimers in tall oil fatty acids. Hase and Harva (42) separated the monomer acid methyl esters from dimers and higher oligomers. Bartosiewicz (43) reported the determination of monomer and dimer acids, but did not describe the method in detail. Inoue (44) accomplished a 24-hr GPC resolution of the methyl esters of monomer acids, dimer acids, and trimer acids. Harris (45), in 1973, achieved GPC separation of monomer acids, dimer acids, and trimer acids in three hours. At about the same time, in related work, Unbehend (46) published a method for the determination of dimeric, trimeric, and higher oligomeric triglycerides in frying fats which had been exposed to extreme thermal oxidation.

Once an accurate determination of monomeric, dimeric, and oligomeric acids has been established on a specific feedstock, viscosity can be used for the fast, approximate determination of extent of polymerization by the method of Sims (47).

C. PHYSICAL PROPERTIES OF DIMER ACIDS

The physical properties of polymerized fatty acids are affected by the raw materials used in manufacture, the dimerization conditions, and the degree to which "monomer", "dimer", and "trimer" are separated. It is obvious that the reaction parameters affect product structure—degree of polymerization, positional isomerism, structural isomerism, among others. It has been amply demonstrated, theoretically and practically, that dimer acids are a mixture of dozens, perhaps hundreds, of molecular species. There has been no comprehensive published literature that describes the relationship of all, or even more than a handful, of the possible reaction variables and the composition, physical properties, and structure of polymerized fatty acids. An excellent beginning of such an exercise is a previously-discussed paper by den Otter (20a), which describes the effect of changes in process parameters (amount of catalyst, water content, stirring intensity, reaction time, and pH) on yield of dimer acids, dimer/trimer ratio, *trans/cis* ratio, acid value, ester value, and other properties. In den Otter's work, oleic acid was the only fatty feedstock used.

Physical properties of commercial dimer and related products are listed in the tables which follow, either as a range of values which are typical, or as an average value.

The products described are those derived from tall oil fatty acids. Experience has shown that some physical properties will be substantially different for dimers based on other fatty acids, such as soya and oleic, even where dimer/trimer ratios are analogous.

Analytical methods have been discussed previously.

Tables 5, 6, 7, 8, and 9 list the physical properties of dimer acids, distilled dimer acids, trimer acids, monomer acids, and isostearic acid. Most commercial producers will supply dimer and trimer acids with any specified addition of monomer acids. This modification will lead to lower product viscosity, lower surface tension, and different polymerization reaction characteristics when the dimer acids are used as a component in polyamide manufacture.

TABLE 5

Properties of Dimer Acids

		Commercial Products		
Physical Characteristics		High Dimer	Intermediate Dimer	High Trimer
Stated Composition {	% Dimer	87	83	75
	% Trimer	13	17	25
	% Monomer	—	—	—
	% Monobasic acids (max.)	1.0	1.0	1.0
Dimer/Trimer mole ratio		10:1	7.3:1	4.5:1
Neutralization equivalent		284-295	287-299	285-297
Acid value		190-198	188-196	188-197
Saponification value		194-200	192-198	190-199
Unsaponifiables, %		0.3-0.5	0.2-1.0	0.3-1.0
Gardner color (1963), maximum		7	8	9
Viscosity {	cSt @ 25°C	5,300-7,600	7,500-8,000	9,000-9,700
	Gardner-Holdt @ 25°C	Z-3 to Z-4	Z-4	Z-5
Specific Gravity {	25°/25°C	0.96	0.95	0.95
	100°/25°C	0.91	0.91	0.93
Density,	lbs/gal @ 25°C	8.0	7.9	8.0
Surface tension (dynes/cm) @ 25°C		26.3-31.9	26.0-33.4	26.3-32.9
Refractive index @ 25°C		1.48	1.48	1.48
Pour point, °F		13-35	24-35	25-35

See Chapter 5 for flash and fire points of dimer acids.

TABLE 6

Properties of Distilled Dimer Acids

Physical Characteristics		Hydrogenated*	Unhydrogenated
Stated Composition	% Dimer	97	95
	% Trimer	3	4
	% Monomer	0	1
	% Monobasic acids(max.)	Nil	1.5
Dimer/Trimer mole ratio		36:1	26:1
Neutralization equivalent		284-294	283-289
Acid value		191-197	194-198
Saponification value		193-200	198-202
Unsaponifiables, %		0.1	0.2-0.5
Gardner color (1963), max.		1	5
Iodine value		20 max.	
Viscosity	cSt @ 25°C	5,200	5,600-6,800
	Gardner-Holdt @ 25°C	Z-3	Z-3 to Z-4
Specific Gravity	25°/25°C	0.94	0.95
	100°/25°C	0.90	0.91
Density,	lbs/gal @ 25°C	7.8	7.9
Surface tension (dynes/cm) @ 25°C		31.1	26.5-31.8
Refractive index @ 25°C		1.48	1.49
Pour point, °F		10	17-35

* From "Empol Dimer and Trimer Acids", Emery Industries, Inc., 1971, used by permission.

TABLE 7

Properties of Trimer Acids

Physical Characteristics		Commercial Properties		
		I	*II**	*III**
Stated Composition	% Dimer	40	20	10
	% Trimer	60	80	90
	% Monomer	—	—	—
	% Monobasic Acids (max.)	1.0	1.0	0
Neutralization equivalent		295-308	294-307	303-387
Acid value		182-190	183-191	145-185
Saponification value		190-198	192-200	170-210
Unsaponifiables, %		1.0	—	—
Gardner color (1963) max.		dark	dark	11
Viscosity	cSt @ 25°C	30,000	60,000	18,000
	Gardner-Holdt @ 25°C	Z-6	Z-6	Z-6
Specific Gravity	25°/25°C	—	0.93	0.94
	100°/25°C	—	0.93	0.90
Density,	lbs/gal @ 25°C	8.0	8.1	7.8
Surface tension (dynes/cm) @ 25°C		27.7	—	—
Refractive index @ 25°C		—	1.50	1.48
Pour point, °F.		—	55	20

See Chapter 5 for flash and fire points of trimer acids.

* From "Empol Dimer and Trimer Acids", Emery Industries, Inc., 1971, used by permission.

TABLE 8

Physical Properties of Monomer Acids
(Industrene M, A Product of Humko Sheffield Chemical)

Specifications

Color	5 Gardner (1963) maximum
Iodine value	80-95
Titer, °C	25-35
Acid value	175-190
Saponification value	180-200
Unsaponifiables, %	5.0 maximum
Moisture, %	0.5 maximum

Hydrogenation of INDUSTRENE M (monomer acids) results in a material which can be separated, by solvent crystallization and subsequent filtration and removal of solvent, into 80% ambient-temperature-liquid fatty acids and 20% material which is solid at room temperature. The liquid fatty acids, with an iodine value <5, are almost entirely branched-chain (or cyclized).

TABLE 9

Properties of Isostearic Acid

	Typical	Specification Minimum	Specification Maximum
Acid value	177	175	
Saponification value	189	180	
Iodine Value	8		10
Titer, °C	6		10
Color, % Transmittance @ 440/550 nm	70/98	30/85	
Color, Gardner (1963)	1		3
Viscosity, cP @ 25°C	50		
Specific gravity, 25/25°C	0.906		
Weight/gallon, lbs	7.55		
Unsaponifiables, %	4		
Moisture, %			

(Century 1105, a product of Union Camp Corporation)

REFERENCES FOR CHAPTER TWO

1. K. Figge, *Chem. Phys. Lipids*, **6**, 159 (1971).
2. R. Guillaumin, *Rev. Fr. Corps Gras*, **17**, 441 (1970).
3. J. C. Cowan, *J. Amer. Oil Chem. Soc.*, **39**, 534 (1962).
4. L. F. Byrne, *Paint Technol.*, **26**, 28 (1962).
5. a. De Nordiske Fabriker, British Patent 127,814 (1919); *Chem. Abs.*, **13**, 2462 (1919).
   b. De Nordiske Fabriker, British Patent 166,236 (1919); *Chem. Abs.*, **16**, 848 (1922).
6. J. Scheiber, *Farbe u. Lack*, **1929**, 585; *Chem. Abs.*, **24**, 978 (1930).
7. C. P. A. Kappelmeier, *Farben-Ztg.*, **38**, 1018 and 1077 (1933); *Chem. Abs.*, **27**, 4425 (1933).
8. T. F. Bradley and W. B. Johnston, *Ind. Eng. Chem.*, **33**, 86 (1941); T. F. Bradley and D. Richardson, *Ind. Eng. Chem.*, **32**, 963 and 802 (1940).
9. C. Boelhouwer, A. C. Jol and H. I. Waterman, *Research*, **5**, 336 (1952); H. I. Waterman, C. J. Kips and J. van Steenis, *Research*, **4**, 96 (1951); H. I. Waterman, J. P. Cordia and B. Pennekamp, *Research*, **2**, 483 (1949).
10. D. H. Wheeler, *Offic. Dig. Fed. Paint and Varnish Prod. Clubs*, **322**, 661 (1951).
11. A. L. Clingman, D. E. A. Rivett and D. A. Sutton, *J. Chem. Soc.* (London), **1954**, 1088.
12. A. H. Kapadi and U. R. Nayak, *Indian J. of Chem.*, **9**, 213 (1971).
13. R. F. Paschke, L. E. Peterson and D. H. Wheeler, *J. Amer. Oil Chem. Soc.*, **41**, 723 (1964).
14. A. K. Sen Gupta and H. Scharmann, *Fette, Seifen, Anstrichm.*, **70**, 86 (1968).
15. D. H. Wheeler and J. White, *J. Amer. Oil Chem. Soc.*, **44**, 298 (1967); R. F. Paschke and D. H. Wheeler, *J. Amer. Oil Chem. Soc.*, **26**, 278 (1949).
16. a. A. K. Sen Gupta, *Fette, Seifen, Anstrichm.*, **70**, 153 and 265 (1968).
    b. A. K. Sen Supta, *Fette, Seifen, Anstrichm.*, **71**, 873 (1969).
17. a. D. H. Wheeler, A. Milun and F. Linn, *J. Amer. Oil Chem. Soc.*, **47**, 242 (1970).
    b. D. H. McMahon and E. P. Crowell, *J. Amer. Oil Chem. Soc.*, **51**, 522 (1974).
18. G. van den Bosch, *J. Amer. Oil Chem. Soc.*, **50**, 421 and 487 (1973); L. H. Brown and R. Swidler, U.S. Patent 3,065,248 (1962).
19. A. K. Sen Gupta, *Fette, Seifen, Anstrichm.*, **69**, 907 (1967).
20. a. M. J. A. M. den Otter, *Fette, Seifen, Anstrichm.*, **72**, 667 (1970).

   b. M. J. A. M. den Otter, *Fette, Seifen, Anstrichm.*, **72,** 875 (1970).

   c. M. J. A. M. den Otter, *Fette, Seifen, Anstrichm.*, **72,** 1056 (1970).

21. H. A. Gardner and P. C. Holdt, "A Standardized Apparatus for Air Bubble Consistency Test on Varnish," Circular No. 128, Paint Manufacturers Assoc. of the U.S., 1921.

22. J. C. Cowan, D. H. Wheeler, H. M. Teeter, R. F. Paschke, C. R. Scholfield, A. W. Schwab, J. E. Jackson, W. C. Bull, F. R. Earle, R. J. Foster, W. C. Bond, R. E. Beal, P. S. Skell, I. A. Wolff and C. Mehltretter, *Ind. Eng. Chem.*, **41,** 1647 (1949).

23. H. P. Kaufman, *Studien auf dem Fettegebiet,* Verlag Chemie, Berlin, 1935, p. 23.

24. A. O. C. S. Method Tg 1a-64T.

25. A. S. T. M. Method D1959-61.

26. D. Firestone, W. Horwitz, L. Friedman and G. G. Shue, *J. Amer. Oil Chem. Soc.*, **44,** 465 (1961); D. Firestone, S. Nesheim and W. Horwitz, *J. Ass. Offic. Anal. Chem.*, **38,** 253 (1961).

27. A. Huang and D. Firestone, *J. Ass. Offic. Anal. Chem.*, **52,** 958 (1969).

28. a. G. Billek and O. Heisz, *Fette, Seifen, Anstrichm.*, **71,** 189 (1969).

   b. D. Firestone, *J. Amer. Oil Chem. Soc.*, **40,** 247 (1963).

29. H. E. Rost, *Fette, Seifen, Anstrichm.*, **65,** 463 (1963); *Fette, Seifen, Anstrichm.*, **64,** 427 (1962).

30. J. C. Cowan, L. B. Falkenburg and H. M. Teeter, *Ind. Eng. Chem., Anal. Ed.*, **16,** 90 (1944).

31. K. C. D. Hickman, *Ind. Eng. Chem.*, **29,** 968 (1937).

32. T. F. Bradley and W. B. Johnston, *Ind. Eng. Chem.*, **33,** 86 (1941).

33. S. A. Harrison and D. H. Wheeler, *J. Amer. Chem. Soc.*, **76,** 2379 (1954).

34. H. Booy and H. I. Waterman, *Anal. Chim. Acta*, **3,** 440 (1949).

35. R. P. A. Sims, *Vacuum*, **2,** 245 (1952).

36. R. F. Paschke, J. R. Kerns and D. H. Wheeler, *J. Amer. Oil Chem. Soc.*, **31,** 5 (1954).

37. E. N. Frankel, C. D. Evans, D. G. McConnell, E. Selke and H. J. Dutton, *J. Org. Chem.*, **26,** 4663 (1961); E. N. Frankel, C. D. Evans, H. A. Moser, D. G. McConnell and J. C. Cowan, *J. Amer. Oil Chem. Soc.*, **38,** 130 (1961); C. D. Evans, D. G. McConnell, E. N. Frankel and J. C. Cowan, *J. Amer. Oil Chem. Soc.*, **42,** 764 (1965).

38. J. H. Greaves and B. Laker, *Chem. Ind.* (London), **1961,** 1709.

39. A. Hase, O. Harva and M. Autio, *Suom. Kemistilehti B*, **42,** 226 (1969).

40. R. A. L. Paylor, R. Feinland and N. H. Conroy, *Anal. Chem.*, **40,** 1358 (1968).

41. T. L. Chang, *Anal. Chem.*, **40,** 989 (1968).

42. A. Hase and O. Harva, *Kem Teollisuus*, **25**, 134 (1968).
43. R. L. Bartosiewicz, *J. Paint Technol.*, **39**, 28 (1967).
44. H. Inoue, K. Konishi and N. Taniguchi, *J. Chromatog.*, **47**, 348 (1970).
45. W. C. Harris, E. P. Crowell and B. B. Burnett, *J. Amer. Oil Chem. Soc.*, **50**, 537 (1973).
46. M. Unbehend, H. Scharmann, H. J. Strauss and G. Billek, *Fette, Seifen, Anstrichm.*, **75**, 689 (1973).
47. R. P. A. Sims, *Ind. Eng. Chem.*, **47**, 1049 (1955).

SUPPLEMENTARY REFERENCES

Herman F. Mark and Norman G. Gaylord, Eds., *Encyclopedia of Polymer Science and Technology*, Vol. 10, Interscience Publishers, Inc., New York, 1969, pp. 599 *ff.*

Raymond E. Kirk and Donald F. Othmer, Eds., *Encyclopedia of Chemical Technology*, 2nd Ed., Vol. 8, Interscience Publishers, Inc., New York, 1965, pp. 847 *ff.*

Klare S. Markley, Ed., *Fatty Acids*, Part 2, Interscience Publishers, Inc., New York, 1961, pp. 1036 *ff.*

O. Suzuki and T. Hashimoto, *Yukagaku*, **18**, 862, 867 and 874 (1969); *J. Amer. Oil Chem. Soc.*, **47** (7), 263A (1970).

S. N. Koley, *Fette Seifen, Anstrichm.*, **73**, 725 (1971).

S. M. A. Ghadssi, J. Petit and H. Valot, *Bull. Soc. Chem. Fr.*, **1970** (4), 1461.

K. Tanabe and T. Hashimoto, *Yukagaku*, **16**, 611 (1967); *J. Amer. Oil Chem. Soc.*, **45** (3), 168A (1968).

F. Neuhaus and I. Temmer, *Rev. Chim.* (Bucharest), **18** (8), 461 (1967); *Chem. Abs.*, **68**, 14302r (1968).

R. F. Paschke, L. E. Peterson, S. A. Harrison and D. H. Wheeler, *J. Amer. Oil Chem. Soc.*, **41**, 56 (1964).

R. F. Paschke and D. H. Wheeler, *J. Amer. Oil Chem. Soc.*, **32**, 469 (1955).

C. G. Goebel, *J. Amer. Oil Chem. Soc.*, **24**, 65 (1947).

H. G. van Raay and M. Teupel, *Fette, Seifen, Anstrichm.*, **75**, 572 (1973).

Chemical Reactions of Dimer Acids

3

Lawrence A. Fury—Humko Sheffield Chemical, Memphis, Tennessee

Earlier in this monograph it was pointed out that dimer acids are predominantly isomers of 36-carbon dibasic acids, with smaller amounts of 54-carbon tribasic acids and still higher-molecular-weight polycarboxylic acids. Dimer acids are unsaturated, containing a statistical average of 1-2 double bonds per molecule.

Dimer acids are capable of undergoing three types of chemical reactions which involve: 1) the carboxyl group, 2) the double bonds, and 3) the carbon atoms adjacent to the carboxyl groups (α-carbons). Except for hydrogenation to saturated, or partially saturated, dimer acids, the only reactions of commercial significance are those involving the carboxylic acid functions. Accordingly, reactions implicating the double bonds and the α-carbons will be mentioned only briefly here.

Dimer acids undergo all of the reactions typical of carboxylic acids. Since they contain more than one carboxylic acid group per molecule, they can be converted to either monomeric or polymeric derivatives, depending on the functionality of the reactants used. Since there are many examples of both monomeric and polymeric derivatives of dimer acids, these will be discussed in separate sections, although the chemical reactions used in their synthesis may be similar.

A. REACTIONS OF THE DOUBLE BONDS AND AT THE α-CARBON ATOMS

Dimer acids typically contain one to two double bonds per molecule as measured by the iodine value, and, being a complex mixture of different structural isomers, may have the double bonds in a ring, or in a side chain, or in both moieties.

Whatever their position within the molecule, the double

bonds appear to be sterically hindered, i.e., react only with difficulty.

Typical reactions involving dimer acids double bonds are the addition of halogens and halogen acids, reaction with sulfuric acid to form alkyl sulfates, sulfurization, oxidation, ozonolysis, epoxidation, and reduction with hydrogen. In most cases, reaction does not proceed to completion. These derivatives have found little commercial value, except for the hydrogenated product (1).

Dimer acids react with atmospheric oxygen, leading to partially oxidized, dark products. Although oxidation of dimer acids does not produce derivatives having commercial utility, prevention of oxidation and concomitant darkening is important commercially. Accordingly, the hydrogenation of the double bonds is commercially important because it deactivates the sites at which undesirable oxidation can occur.

Hydrogenation of the double bonds in dimer acids can be effected with a variety of catalysts. These include nickel, cobalt, platinum, palladium, and rhenium. Depending on the activity of the catalyst and the conditions used, partial saturation or complete saturation of the double bonds can result (2, 3). The observation that catalysts with different activities effect different degrees of saturation is one indication that the double bonds present in dimer acids have different reactivities.

In addition to reactions involving double bonds, it is also possible to cause dimer acids to react at the carbon atoms adjacent to the carboxylic acid groups (α-carbons). Reactions such as bromination and sulfonation (4) are known, but products of reaction at the α-carbons are of little commercial value.

B. REACTIONS OF THE CARBOXYL GROUPS TO PRODUCE MONOMERIC DERIVATIVES

Dimer acids are capable of reactions with monofunctional reactants. The reactions are typical of carboxylic acids, each acid group in the molecule reacting independently of the other. Thus, conversion of dimer acids to monomeric derivatives is similar to the reactions of monobasic fatty acids.

1. *Formation of Metal Soaps and Metallic Salts*

The dimer acids undergo reaction with sodium, potassium, and lithium hydroxides to form water-soluble soaps, and, with alkaline earth and heavy metal oxides or hydroxides such as those of aluminum, calcium, zinc, lead, magnesium, barium, and cadmium, to form water-insoluble metallic salts.

In their reaction with alkali metal hydroxides, dimer acids resemble any typical fatty acid (5):

$$R(COOH)_2 + 2MOH \longrightarrow \overset{+}{M}\overset{-}{O}\overset{O}{\overset{\|}{C}}R\overset{O}{\overset{\|}{C}}\overset{-}{O}\overset{+}{M} + 2H_2O$$

Since the ratio of hydrocarbon chain/carboxyl group is approximately the same for both dimer acids and stearic or oleic acid, the dimer acids soaps have similar solubilities in aqueous solution to soaps prepared from stearic and oleic acids.

Metallic salts of dimer acids are prepared similarly to salts of monobasic fatty acids, either by direct reaction with metallic oxides or hydroxides (direct fusion) or by the conversion of the dimer acids to an alkali metal soap, followed by reaction with a solution of the appropriate metallic salt (metathesis) (6):

Direct Fusion

$$R(COOH)_2 + M(OH)_2 \longrightarrow \overset{-}{-}\left(\overset{}{O}\overset{O}{\overset{\|}{C}}R\overset{O}{\overset{\|}{C}}\overset{-}{O}\overset{++}{M}\right)_x\overset{}{-} + 2H_2O$$

   (or MO)

Double Decomposition

(1) $R(COOH)_2 + 2MOH \longrightarrow \overset{+}{M}\overset{-}{O}\overset{O}{\overset{\|}{C}}R\overset{O}{\overset{\|}{C}}\overset{-}{O}\overset{+}{M} + 2H_2O$

(2) $\overset{+}{M}\overset{-}{O}\overset{O}{\overset{\|}{C}}R\overset{O}{\overset{\|}{C}}\overset{-}{O}\overset{+}{M} + \overset{++}{M} \longrightarrow -\left(\overset{-}{O}\overset{O}{\overset{\|}{C}}R\overset{O}{\overset{\|}{C}}\overset{-}{O}\overset{++}{M}\right)_x\overset{}{-} + 2\overset{+}{M}$

Since dimer acids are polyfunctional and the carboxyl group has an effective valence of one, the metallic salts of dimer acids are probably polymeric rather than monomeric, as indicated in these equations. The salts have properties similar to metallic salts of monobasic fatty acids, however, including solubility in organic solvents.

2. Esterification

Dimer acids react readily with a variety of monofunctional alcohols to produce esters:

$$R(COOH)_2 + 2R'OH \overset{H^+}{\longrightarrow} R(COOR')_2 + 2H_2O$$

Typically, the esterification is catalyzed by strong acids such as sulfuric and p-toluenesulfonic acid and, although reversible, the reaction can be driven to completion either by using an excess of alcohol or by removing the water formed by distillation (7).

A large variety of alcohols can be used to form esters of dimer acids. Among these are methanol, ethanol, isopropanol, 2-ethylhexanol, long-chain fatty alcohols, and branched-chain alcohols (8, 9). Dimer acids esters are normally nonviscous liquids, and are soluble in a variety of solvents, including hydrocarbon lubricating oils. The low-molecular-weight esters (e.g., methyl) of the dimer acids are often used to make other derivatives of dimer acids.

3. *Reduction to Alcohols*

The dimer acids or the methyl esters can be converted to the corresponding dimer alcohols by hydrogenation:

$$R(COOH)_2 \xrightarrow{\text{H}_2} R(CH_2OH)_2 + 2H_2O$$

$$R(COOR')_2 \xrightarrow{\text{H}_2} R(CH_2OH)_2 + 2R'OH$$

Reduction is normally effected using high-pressure hydrogenation in the presence of catalysts such as copper chromite (10, 11).

The dimer alcohols are viscous liquids. They are miscible with organic solvents and form emulsions with water. Conversion of the carboxyl group to the alcohol group increases the number of derivatives possible from dimer acids, since the dimer alcohols undergo reactions typical of other fatty alcohols. Both monomeric and polymeric derivatives can be prepared.

4. *Ethoxylation*

Dimer acids may be reacted with ethylene oxide and other oxiranes to produce alkoxylated derivatives. The initial reaction product is the hydroxyethyl ester, and, if proper reaction conditions are used, the bis(hydroxyethyl) dimer ester is the major product (12):

$$R(COOH)_2 + 2CH_2\underset{O}{\overset{}{\diagdown\!\!\diagup}}CH_2 \longrightarrow R(COOCH_2CH_2OH)_2$$

The hydroxyethyl ester can also react with ethylene oxide, so that varying amounts of polyoxyethylene esters are present along with the bis(hydroxyethyl) esters. The bis-(hydroxyethyl) esters of dimer acids are miscible with organic solvents and immiscible with water. Since they contain available hydroxyl groups, they are capable of further reactions typical of alcohols. As expected, they are subject to hydrolysis at the ester linkage.

By using excess ethylene oxide, dimer acids can be converted to polyoxyethylene esters (13, 14):

$$HO(CH_2)_2 (OCH_2CH_2)_mOCORCOO (CH_2CH_2O)_n(CH_2)_2OH$$

As the length of the oxyethylene chain increases, these esters increase in water miscibility, so that it is possible to produce both water-dispersible and water-miscible derivatives.

Polyoxyethylene esters of dimer acids may also be prepared by the reaction of dimer acids with polyethylene glycols (15) derived from the polymerization of ethylene oxide. Using the glycols, small quantities of polyesters are also formed, but the esters prepared in this way are very similar in properties to those prepared by direct ethoxylation.

5. *Formation of Nitrogen Derivatives*

Dimer acids react with ammonia and monofunctional amines to produce salts, amides, substituted amides, amines, and nitriles. The reactions are typical of fatty acids in general.

a. *Formation of Ammonium Soaps and Amine Salts*

Reactions of dimer acids with aqueous ammonia produces the ammonium soaps, which are soluble in water.

Reaction of dimer acids with primary, secondary, or tertiary amines produces amine salts of dimer acids, which typically are emulsifiable with water or soluble in organic solvents. A large variety of amines can be used, such as the methylamines and other low-molecular-weight primary, secondary, and tertiary amines, fatty amines and diamines, and heterocyclic amines such as piperazine and morpholine (16).

b. *Formation of Amides and Substituted Amides*

Dimer acids can be converted to primary amides, either by the controlled dehydration of ammonium soaps, or by reaction of the methyl esters with ammonia:

$$R(COONH_4)_2 \xrightarrow{\Delta} R(CONH_2)_2 + 2H_2O$$

$$R(COOCH_3)_2 + 2NH_3 \xrightarrow{\Delta} R(CONH_2)_2 + 2CH_3OH$$

These primary amides are waxy, low-melting solids, which

are soluble in organic solvents. They are difficult to prepare in good yields.

Similarly, amides of the dimer acids, substituted on the nitrogen, can be prepared using a variety of substituted amines, either directly from the acid or from the methyl ester:

$$R(COOH)_2 + 2R'_2NH \longrightarrow R(CONR'_2)_2 + 2H_2O$$

$$R(COOCH_3)_2 + 2R'_2NH \longrightarrow R(CONR'_2)_2 + 2CH_3OH$$

Specific examples of dimer acids/amine reactions include those involving dimethylamine, N,N-dimethylaminopropylamine, piperidine, and diethanolamine (17, 18, 19, 20, 21):

(1) $R(COOH)_2 + 2(CH_3)_2NH \longrightarrow R[CON(CH_3)_2]_2 + 2H_2O$

(2) $R(COOH)_2 + H_2NCH_2CH_2CH_2N(CH_3)_2 \longrightarrow$

$$R[CONHCH_2CH_2CH_2N(CH_3)_2]_2 + 2H_2O$$

(3) $R(COOH)_2 + 2 \langle NH \longrightarrow R(CON \rangle)_2 + 2H_2O$

(4) $R(COOH)_2 + 2NH(CH_2CH_2OH)_2 \longrightarrow$

$$R[CON(CH_2CH_2OH)_2]_2 + 2H_2O$$

As with other derivatives of dimer acids, the amides are miscible with organic solvents and immiscible with water. The alkanolamide derivatives of dimer acids can be ethoxylated, leading to water-miscible or water-dispersible products (17, 22).

c. *Formation of Nitriles and Conversion to Amines*

The ammonium salts of dimer acids can be converted to the corresponding nitriles by dehydration, using more stringent conditions than in the formation of amides:

$$R(COONH_4)_2 \xrightarrow[H_3PO_4]{\Delta} R(CN)_2 + 4H_2O$$

Reaction occurs readily at elevated temperatures in the presence of dehydration catalysts such as phosphoric acid and phosphorus pentoxide. The yield of nitrile is usually high, since the nitrile group is the final product of dehydration of the ammonium salts (23, 24).

The dimer nitriles are useful intermediates for the preparation of a variety of amines. Hydrogenation of the nitrile in the presence of ammonia produces primary amines (25):

$$R(CN)_2 + 4H_2 \xrightarrow{NH_3} R(CH_2NH_2)_2$$

The ammonia is used to minimize the formation of secondary and tertiary amines. The dimer diprimary amines are nonviscous liquids, and are miscible with organic solvents. They can be converted to a variety of derivatives, both monomeric and polymeric. Because the polymeric derivatives are of special interest, they will be discussed in a separate section.

Dimer diprimary amine can be reacted with acrylonitrile followed by reduction with hydrogen and ammonia to produce the tetraamine (25):

$$R(CH_2NH_2)_2 + 2CH_2{=}CHCN \longrightarrow$$
$$R(CH_2NHCH_2CH_2CN)_2$$
$$R(CH_2NHCH_2CH_2CN)_2 + 4H_2 \xrightarrow{NH_3}$$
$$R(CH_2NHCH_2CH_2CH_2NH_2)_2$$

The resulting tetraamines, again, are capable of undergoing a variety of reactions. These reactions have included formation of salts; alkylation to produce secondary amines, tertiary amines, and quaternary ammonium salts; ethoxylation; and other reactions typical of fatty amines and diamines.

6. Other Monomeric Derivatives of Dimer Acids

Dimer acids can be converted to the acid chloride and to the isocyanate.

a. Formation of Acid Chlorides

Dimer acids can be converted to acid chlorides by the general methods used for fatty acid chloride synthesis (26, 27):

1) reaction with thionyl chloride,

$$R(COOH)_2 + 2SOCl_2 \longrightarrow R(COCl)_2 + 2SO_2 + 2HCl$$

2) reaction with phosphorus pentachloride,

$$R(COOH)_2 + 2PCl_5 \longrightarrow R(COCl)_2 + 2HCl + 2POCl_3$$

3) reaction with phosphorus trichloride,

$$3R(COOH)_2 + 2PCl_3 \longrightarrow 3R(COCl)_2 + 2H_3PO_3$$

4) reaction with oxalyl chloride,

$$R(COOH)_2 + 2(COCl)_2 \longrightarrow R(COCl)_2 + 2CO_2 + 2CO + 2HCl$$

The dimer acid chlorides, like other high-molecular-weight acid chlorides, are water immiscible and relatively stable in the presence of moisture (26). They are corrosive towards metals, and are useful mainly as intermediates in making other derivatives.

b. *Formation of Isocyanates*

Dimer acids can be converted to isocyanates, either by the reaction of the acid chlorides with sodium azide (27) or by the reaction of dimer diprimary amine with phosgene:

1) $R(COCl)_2 + 2NaN_3 \longrightarrow R(CON_3)_2 + 2NaCl$

   $R(CON_3)_2 \xrightarrow{\Delta} R(NCO)_3 + 2N_2$

2) $R(CH_2NH_2)_2 + 2COCl_2 \longrightarrow$

   $R(CH_2NCO)_2 + 4HCl$

The polymers from dimer diisocyanates are described in Section C of this chapter.

C. REACTIONS OF THE CARBOXYL GROUPS TO PRODUCE POLYMERIC DERIVATIVES

Condensation polymerization reactions will convert dimer acids to many different types of polymeric products. This family of compounds can produce an even larger number of polymers if condensation polymerizations based on dimer acids derivatives are carried out.

Commercially-available dimer acids are not made up entirely of chemically pure difunctional acids. Although manufacturing procedures are carefully controlled, the process inherently leads to the formation of mixtures of polybasic acids. The mixture of acids present in dimer acids has an average acid functionality greater than two. Consequently, polymers produced from commercial dimer acids possess some amount of cross-linked three-dimensional structure. The cross-linking can be controlled to some extent by the use of monofunctional molecules to balance the polybasic acids present. Because of the cross-linking, dimer acids polymers are relatively low-molecular-weight products.

Historically, the major contribution to the present understanding of condensation polymerization was the work of W. H. Carothers of E. I. duPont de Nemours and Co., Inc. (28). Dr. Carothers began research in 1929 on the reaction of dibasic acids with aliphatic diamines and glycols. This brilliant and uniquely successful work eventually led to the commercial development of both polyamide and polyester fibers and resins. In addition to determining that condensation polymers were formed by the regular growth of repeating units, Carothers was able to show that the properties of the polymers formed were dependent upon such factors as the functional purity of the reactants used, their chemical structure, and the stoichiometry of the reaction. To understand the polymerization reactions of the dimer acids, it is worthwhile to review the main scientific contributions of Carothers and his collaborators:

(1) Reaction of one monomer containing two functional groups with another monomer containing two functional groups leads to the formation of a linear polymer.

(2) Reaction of one monomer with two functional groups with another monomer with more than two functional groups leads to a three-dimensional branched-chain polymer. Reaction usually proceeds to a sharp gel point, due to the build-up of a molecular network.

(3) Monofunctional molecules tend to act as chain stoppers, limiting molecular weight build-up in linear polymers and decreasing the amount of cross-linking which occurs in three-dimensional polymers. Use of monofunctional molecules allows some control over the type of polymer formed.

(4) The stoichiometry of the reaction is vitally important. Normally, equivalent amounts of each reactant are used to produce a neutral polymer with the highest possible molecular weight. An excess of either reactant causes an effect similar to that exerted by a monofunctional molecule, essentially terminating the reaction and yielding a polymer lower in molecular weight than if exact equivalents were used.

(5) The molecular weight and the chemical structure of the reactants used have a pronounced effect on the properties of the polymer. As the molecular weight of the reactants increases, the relative amount of the molecular weight contributed by the functional groups decreases, and the polymer reflects more of the non-functional group portion of the reactants. For example, nylon 6, 6 (made from adipic acid and hexamethylenediamine) melts at 265°C, while nylon 6,10 (made from sebacic acid and hexamethylenediamine) melts at 215°C, even though the molecular weights of the two polymers are about the same (29). The effect of branching is sim-

ilar; thus the polyamide made from α-methyladipic acid and hexamethylenediamine melts at 166°C, in comparison with nylon 6,6 at 265°C (30). The polyamide made from dimer acids and hexamethylenediamine melts at about 70-80°C.

In considering the various types of polymers made from dimer acids, it is important to emphasize that dimer acids have a high molecular weight (575-625), and are not purely difunctional. The polymers made from them are usually of low molecular weight, and they contain cross-linked molecules. Because of the complex structure of the mixture of acids present in commercial dimer acids, the polymers made from them are normally low-melting solids or liquids. The properties of the polymers reflect largely the hydrocarbon nature of dimer acids. Most of the end-products, as a result, are resistant to moisture and to a variety of chemicals. Resins and films are flexible and durable.

1. *Polyamide Resins Based on Dimer Acids*

Dimer acids may be reacted with a variety of polyfunctional amines to produce polyamide resins. These polyamides range from nonreactive, sharp-melting neutral solids to reactive liquids, depending on the choice of polyfunctional amine used.

The large number of polyfunctional amines capable of forming polyamide resins can be classified into two categories: 1) difunctional amines (only two amino groups, usually primary), and 2) polyfunctional amines (more than two amino groups, usually containing two *primary* amino groups). Examples of difunctional amines are ethylenediamine, propylenediamine, 1,3-diaminopropane, hexamethylenediamine, and *p*-phenylenediamine. Examples of polyfunctional amines are diethylenetriamine, triethylenetetramine, tetraethylenepentamine, and pentaethylenehexamine.

The reaction of dimer acids with difunctional amines produces *neutral* polyamides:

$$R(COOH)_2 + R'(NH_2)_2 \longrightarrow -(-CORCONHR'NH-)_n-$$

Reaction of dimer acids with polyfunctional amines produces *reactive* polyamides:

$$R(COOH)_2 + H_2N-(-CH_2CH_2NH-)_x-CH_2CH_2NH_2 \longrightarrow$$
$$-(-CORCONH-(-CH_2CH_2NH-)_x-CH_2CH_2NH-)_n-$$

The amine used can be considered to have the equivalent weight of a diamine for stoichiometric calculation. Theoretically, only primary amino groups react with the carboxyl groups of dimer acids. In the case of polyamides from polyfunctional amines, the remaining secondary amino groups not reacted with dimer acids are available for further reaction, and hence are designated as *reactive* polyamides.

Polyamide resins made from dimer acids are normally either low-melting solids or liquids, depending on the diamine used. The melting ranges of some typical polyamides are given in the following tables. In the case of the reactive polyamides, the amine value (measure of unreacted amino groups) is also given (31, 32).

TABLE 10

Melting Ranges for Typical Neutral Polyamides

Dimer/ Trimer Mole Ratio	Diamine	Stoichiometry (dimer/amine)	Polyamide Melting Range
1.7:1	ethylenediamine	equivalent	96-103°C
1.8:1	ethylenediamine	equivalent	108-112°C
1.7:1	propylenediamine	equivalent	53-59°C
1.7:1	hexamethylenediamine	equivalent	70-80°C
1.7:1	dimer diprimary amine	equivalent	liquid

TABLE 11

Melting Ranges for Typical Reactive Polyamides

Dimer/ Trimer Mole Ratio	Polyamine	Stoichiometry (as diamine)	Polyamide Melting Range	Amine Value
1.7:1	diethylenetriamine	equivalent	50-56°C	*ca.* 80
1.7:1	tetraethylenepentamine	equivalent	45-50°C	*ca.* 250
1.7:1	mixture of ethylenediamine and diethylenetriamine	equivalent	60-70°C	*ca.* 40-80

From these data the following general observations can be made:

(1) Polyamides made from dimer acids and ethylenediamine, with sufficient monobasic acid to prevent crosslinking, usually melt in the range 100-120°C. The melting

range is affected only slightly by the composition of the dimer acids used, although the melting range is usually more narrow when higher purity dimer acids are used.

(2) Diamines other than ethylenediamine give polyamides having lower melting points.

    a. In the case of diprimary diamines, this effect is observed both in diamines of higher molecular weight and in diamines with branched-chain structures.

    b. In the case of polyamines, the melting point is lowered as the molecular weight of the polyamine increases.

In most cases, the molecular weights of the polyamides described in Tables 10 and 11 are in the range 5,000 to 10,000, and they are not affected significantly by the amine used.

In preparing polyamide resins, the dimer acids may be the only dibasic acid used, or it may be mixed with other dibasic acids, giving copolyamides. The data in Table 12 (31) show clearly that the temperature at which the polyamide begins to melt increases as the ratio of sebacic acid to dimer acid increases.

TABLE 12

Effect of Short-Chain Dibasic Acids on Polyamide Melting Range

Dimer/ Trimer[a] (% of total acid)	Sebacic Acid (% of total acid)	Diamine[b]	Polyamide Melting Range
100	0	ethylenediamine	108-112°C
87.5	12.5	ethylenediamine	122-129°C
75	25	ethylenediamine	146-155°C
50	50	ethylenediamine	188-196°C

(a) Dimer/Trimer mole ratio 1.8:1; (b) Diamine used in equivalent amounts to total acid used.

The increase in melting point is attributed to the increase in intermolecular attraction between individual polymer molecules, due to hydrogen bonding and van der Waals forces. The molecular weights of polyamides produced using short-chain dibasic acids as coreactants are in the range 5,000 to 15,000, similar to other dimer acids-based polyamides.

The polyamide resins produced from dimer acids, both

neutral and reactive, are the most important commercial derivatives of the dimer acids. Their applications will be discussed in Chapter 4.

2. *Reactions of Reactive Polyamides*

The reactive polyamides function chemically as polyamines, and thus are capable of undergoing further reactions with a variety of other reactants. The reactions of reactive polyamides with epoxy compounds and with phenolic resins are typical examples (33):

$$...CORCONH-(-CH_2CH_2NH-)_n-CH_2CH_2NH...+$$

$$CH_2-CH-R'CH-CH_2- \longrightarrow$$
$$\diagdown O \diagup \qquad \diagdown O \diagup$$

$$...CORCONH-(-CH_2CH_2N-)_n-CH_2CH_2NH...$$
$$| $$
$$CH_2$$
$$| $$
$$CHOH$$
$$| $$
$$R'$$
$$| $$
$$CHOH$$
$$| $$
$$CH_2$$
$$| $$
$$...CORCONH-(-CH_2CH_2N-)_n-CH_2CH_2NH...$$

Reaction of the polyamide with the epoxy compound occurs very readily and can be carried out either by heating the mixture to a homogenous melt or dissolving in a solvent (34). When a melt is used, reaction begins immediately and is complete in a few hours. When solvents are used, polymerization occurs more slowly, and it is possible to store the solvent mixture for several days without excessive reaction occurring.

As the polyamide and the epoxy compound react, a polymer containing both hydroxyl groups and amino groups is formed. As the reaction proceeds, the remaining epoxy groups can react with either of these, resulting in a complex cross-linked polymer. The ratio of epoxide to polyamide can be varied over a wide range, giving resins which vary in properties from flexible rubbery products to hard durable solids.

Reactive polyamides also undergo reaction with phenol-formaldehyde condensates (35).

$$\ldots CORCONH \overbrace{(CH_2CH_2NH)}_{n} CH_2CH_2NH \ldots$$

$$+ \; HOCH_2 - \underset{CH_2OH}{\overset{CH_2OH}{\bigcirc}} - OH \longrightarrow$$

$$\ldots CORCONH \overbrace{(CH_2CH_2N)}_{n} CH_2CH_2NH \ldots$$

$$\ldots CH_2 - \bigcirc - OH \; + \; H_2O$$

Reaction occurs between the amino groups of the polyamide and the resin, producing a highly cross-linked product.

In contrast to the epoxy-polyamide resins, phenolic-polyamide mixtures are less reactive, and heat must be applied to cause reaction. Blends of the phenolic-polyamide resins are stable in solution for extended periods, unless exposed to heat (35).

3. *Polyester Resins Based on Dimer Acids*

The dimer acids react readily with a variety of glycols and polyols to produce polyester resins:

$$R(COOH)_2 + R'(CH_2OH)_2 \longrightarrow$$
$$(CORCOOCH_2R'CH_2O)_x + 2H_2O$$

Polyesters based on dimer acids are typically viscous fluids, with molecular weights ranging from 5,000 to 30,000. When polyols are used, or when the polyfunctional acids present are not balanced by monobasic acids, rubbery, cross-linked solid polyester resins are obtained. When simple glycols are used, such as ethylene glycol, propylene glycol, and decamethylene glycol, the polyesters are normally oil soluble (36). When polymeric glycols are used, such as the polyoxyalkylene glycols (polyethylene glycol, polypropylene glycol), the resulting polyesters can range from water dispersible to water miscible (37, 38).

The dimer acids can also be used with a variety of other dibasic acids to form mixed polyesters. Thus, mixtures of dimer acids with dibasic acids such as phthalic acid (or anhydride), maleic acid, fumaric acid, terephthalic acid, adipic acid, and sebacic acid, may be reacted with polyols to form polyesters. Depending on the relative amounts (39, 40) of dibasic acids used, the mixed polyesters exhibit properties intermediate between the polyesters made using only one dibasic acid.

Polyesters based on dimer acids can be made using equivalent amounts of acid and glycol, or they can be prepared using an excess of either reactant. By using an excess of one reactant, polyesters can be formed which contain terminal acid or hydroxyl groups, which are capable of further reaction. These reactive polyesters are usually lower in molecular weight than polyesters made using equivalent amounts of reactants. They are suitable for reaction with other polymers, however, to form more complex polymers and resins.

4. Reactions of Hydroxy-Terminated Dimer Acids Derivatives

A number of literature references describe dimer acids-based polyesters which are made using polyols. These polyesters, containing terminal hydroxyl groups, are capable of undergoing further reaction. In this respect, they are similar to the reactive polyamides. In addition, the hydroxyalkyl polyether esters, made by reacting dimer acids with excess ethylene oxide (13, 14), also contain terminal hydroxyl groups, and they react similarly to the hydroxy-terminated polyesters. By converting the dimer acids to hydroxy-containing derivatives, they can be incorporated into polymers such as polycarbonates and polyurethanes (12, 13, 14, 15, 41, 42, 43).

To produce polycarbonates, dihydroxy compounds are reacted with phosgene (41):

$$R'(CH_2OH)_2 + COCl_2 \longrightarrow$$

$$\overset{O}{\overset{\|}{-\!\!\left(\!-OCOCH_2R'CH_2\!-\!\right)_{\!x}\!-}} + 2HCl$$

In other polycarbonate systems, dihydroxydiaryl compounds such as 4, 4'-dihydroxydiphenylmethane are used, and the finished product is a high-molecular-weight rigid polymer. In contrast, polycarbonates made from hydroxy-terminated dimer acid derivatives, either as the major diol or as a component along with other diols, are more flexible products, and are normally lower in molecular weight (41, 44).

In the formation of polyurethanes, the initial reaction is between a dihydroxy compound and an aryl diisocyanate, forming a prepolymer containing urethane bonds:

$$R(CH_2OH)_2 + 2\ (\!\!-\!\!\langle\ \rangle\!\!-\!\!NCO)_2 \longrightarrow$$

$$R\!\!-\!\!(\!\!-\!\!\overset{O}{\overset{\|}{CH_2OCNH}}\!\!\langle\ \rangle\!\!-\!\!\langle\ \rangle\!\!-\!\!NCO)_2$$

The isocyanate group reacts readily with any functional group containing reactive hydrogen atoms (such as amines, alcohols, urethanes, and water). Once the reaction is initiated, a very complex polymer is produced. If water is present, reaction of the water (45) with the isocyanate generates carbon dioxide, resulting in the formation of a foamed product.

The dihydroxy compounds most commonly used to react with the aryl diisocyanate are low-molecular-weight hydroxy-terminated polyesters, and polyether polyols such as polyethylene glycol or polypropylene glycol.

Suitable polyesters can also be made using dimer acids, leading to polyurethanes which possess excellent flexibility and impact resistance characteristics and which are resistant to moisture and chemicals (46, 47, 48).

The hydroxyethyl esters of dimer acids may also be used to produce polyurethanes. Other hydroxy-terminated derivatives of dimer acids may also be used, including alkanolamide derivatives made by reacting dimer acids with mono-ethanolamine or diethanolamine (49).

5. *Polymeric Nitrogen Derivatives of Dimer Acids*

In addition to the formation of polyamide resins by the reaction of dimer acids with polyamines, it is possible to prepare a variety of other types of polymeric nitrogen derivatives of the dimer acids. The key intermediate is the dimer nitrile, prepared from dimer acids by the dehydration of the ammonium salt:

$$R(COONH_4)_2 \longrightarrow R(CN)_2 + 4H_2O$$

The dimer nitrile can be used directly to form polymeric, secondary amines, tertiary amines, and quaternary ammonium salts (23, 24). It can also be converted to dimer diprimary amine, from which additional polymeric products can be prepared.

    a. *Formation of Polymeric Secondary Amines From Dimer Nitrile*

    By using conditions favoring the formation of secondary amines, dimer nitrile can be converted directly to a polymeric secondary amine (50):

$$R(CN)_2 \xrightarrow[\text{catalyst}]{H_2} H_2N\!-\!\!\left(\!-CH_2RCH_2NH\right)_{\!x}\!\!-\!H$$

Depending on the reaction conditions used, the yield of polymeric secondary amine can be quite high, and the polymers can vary in chain length from two molecules to as many as forty or more. The lower-molecular-weight products are nonviscous liquids, and the viscosity increases as the molecular weight increases. The polymers are normally soluble in organic solvents.

    b. *Formation of Polymeric Tertiary Amines and Quaternary Ammonium Compounds*

    Although it is possible to form polymeric tertiary amines from the dimer nitrile itself, the polymers are highly cross-linked, infusible resins. However, polymeric tertiary amines can be produced by reacting the polymeric secondary amines with the appropriate alkylating agent (51):

$$-\!\!\left(\!-CH_2RCH_2NH\!-\right)_{\!x}\!\! + R'Cl \longrightarrow$$
$$-\!\!\left(\!-CH_2RCH_2\underset{\underset{R'}{|}}{N}\!-\right)_{\!x}\!\! + HCl$$

    The polymeric tertiary amine can be isolated as such, or it can be reacted with additional alkylating agent to form polymeric quaternary ammonium compounds (52):

$$-\!\!\left(\!-CH_2RCH_2\underset{\underset{R'}{|}}{N}\!-\right)_{\!x}\!\! + R''Cl \longrightarrow -\!\!\left(\!-CH_2RCH_2\overset{\overset{R''Cl^-}{|}}{\underset{\underset{R'}{|}}{N^+}}\!-\right)_{\!x}$$

    By using excess alkylating agent, it is possible to produce quaternary ammonium compounds in which both alkyl groups are the same. It is also possible to isolate the tertiary amine, and then form quaternary ammonium compounds with different alkylating agents, so that the alkyl groups are different. Both the tertiary amines and the quaternary ammonium salts are viscous liquids, and are soluble in organic solvents.

   c. *Polymeric Reactions Involving Dimer Diprimary Amine*

Dimer diprimary amine is produced by the controlled reduction of dimer nitrile, using conditions favoring the formation of primary amines. Yields of primary amine are usually high, with small amounts of secondary amines also being formed.

The dimer diprimary amine reacts as do other diamines, and a variety of polymers can be prepared from it. The most typical example is the formation of polyamide resins, by reacting dimer diprimary amine with dibasic acids (53, 54):

$$R(CH_2NH_2)_2 + R'(COOH)_2 \longrightarrow$$

$$-\!\!\left(\!-\!\overset{O}{\overset{\|}{C}}R'\overset{O}{\overset{\|}{C}}NHCH_2RCH_2NH\!-\!\right)_{\!\!x} + 2H_2O$$

A variety of dibasic acids can be used, such as adipic acid, sebacic acid, dimer acids, and terephthalic acid. In addition, mixtures of dibasic acids and/or mixtures of diamines may be used to produce copolymers. The properties of the polyamides made using dimer diprimary amine are very similar to those using dimer acids, and the factors which affect the properties of dimer acids-based polyamides also affect the properties of dimer diamine-based polyamides.

An interesting series of polymers can be made by converting either dimer acid chlorides or dimer diprimary amine to the corresponding dimer diisocyanate (27). The isocyanate can be prepared from the dimer acid chlorides by reaction with sodium azide, or from the dimer diprimary amine by reaction with phosgene (27). These reactions were discussed earlier.

The dimer diisocyanates undergo reactions typical of other isocyanates, and thus they can be converted to polymers such as polyurethanes by reaction with polyhydric alcohols, and to polyureas by reaction with polyfunctional amines (55). The polymeric nitrogen derivatives of dimer acids are relatively new developments, and they expand significantly the scope of reactions which the dimer acids undergo.

6. *Miscellaneous Polymeric Reactions of Dimer Acids*

   Among other polymeric reactions which dimer acids undergo are those involving the direct reaction of dimer acids with polyepoxides, and the reaction of dimer acids to form monomeric epoxy derivatives which can then be reacted further.

The dimer acids and the trimer acids can be reacted directly with diepoxides, resulting in the formation of a complex cross-linked resin (56). A variety of polyepoxides can be used, and the resulting resins exhibit good flexibility and resistance to moisture and chemicals.

It is also possible to convert dimer acids to monomeric epoxy derivatives, by reaction of epichlorohydrin with dimer acids or their sodium soaps (57). These monomeric epoxy derivatives are capable of further reactions typical of other epoxy compounds. As with other polymers based on dimer acids, these resins exhibit good flexibility, impact resistance, and resistance to moisture and chemicals.

The polymeric reactions of dimer acids and the derivatives of dimer acids are probably used to produce more different types of polymers for commercial applications than is the case for any other dibasic acid. This utilization, based on the unique combination of carboxylic acid functionality and the presence of a large hydrocarbon moiety, accounts for consumption of millions of pounds of dimer acids annually. The applications of dimer acids will be discussed in Chapter 4.

REFERENCES FOR CHAPTER THREE

1. For examples of reactions of unsaturated fatty acids see Daniel Swern, Ed., *Bailey's Industrial Oil and Fat Products,* 3rd Edition, Interscience Publishers, Inc., New York, 1964, pp. 62-68.
2. M. V. Kulkarni and R. L. Scheribel, U.S. Patent 3,595,887 (1971).
3. E. M. Fischer and F. M. Linn, U.S. Patent 3,256,304 (1966).
4. For an example of this reaction of a fatty acid, see "Sulfur Derivatives," in Klare S. Markley, Ed., *Fatty Acids,* Part 3, 2nd Edition, Interscience Publishers, Inc., New York, 1964, p. 1746.
5. See Reference 1, p. 59.
6. J. Levy, "Utilization of Fatty Acids in Metallic Soaps and Greases," in E. Scott Pattison, Ed., *Fatty Acids and Their Industrial Applications,* Marcel Dekker, Inc., New York, 1968, p. 209.
7. See Reference 1, p. 56, for a general discussion of fatty acid esterification.
8. A. J. Morway, D. W. Young and D. L. Cottle, U.S. Patent 2,673,184 (1954).
9. A. H. Matuszak and W. J. Craven, U.S. Patent 2,849,399 (1958).
10. W. B. Johnston, U.S. Patent 2,347,562 (1944).
11. E. W. Eckey and J. E. Taylor, U.S. Patent 2,413,612 (1946).
12. T. E. Yeates and C. M. Thierfelder, U.S. Patent 3,173,887 (1965).
13. R. H. Kienle and G. P. Whitcomb, U.S. Patent 2,473,798 (1949).
14. G. E. Barker, U.S. Patent 2,758,976 (1956); 2,755,251 (1956).
15. M. J. Furey and A. F. Turbak, U.S. Patent 3,429,817 (1969).
16. For a discussion of the formation of fatty nitrogen chemicals from fatty acids, see E. Scott Pattison, Ed., *Fatty Acids and Their Industrial Applications,* Marcel Dekker, Inc., New York, 1968, pp. 77-154.
17. J. T. Thurston and R. B. Warner, U.S. Patent 2,537,493 (1951); 2,470,081 (1949).
18. C. E. Santangelo and B. H. Kress, U.S. Patent 2,992,145 (1961).
19. G. F. Scherer, U.S. Patent 3,256,182 (1966).
20. J. Dazzi, U.S. Patent 2,965,591 (1960).
21. E. L. Skau, R. R. Mod and F. C. Magne, U.S. Patent 3,219,612 (1965); 3,336,319 (1967).
22. L. A. Fluck and A. L. Logan, U.S. Patent 2,718,478 (1955).

23. A. W. Ralston, O. Turinsky and C. W. Christensen, U.S. Patent 2,526,044 (1950).
24. A. J. Morway and A. J. Rutkowski, U.S. Patent 3,223,631 (1965).
25. K. E. McCaleb, L. Vertnik and D. L. Andersen, U.S. Patent 3,010,782 (1961).
26. N. O. V. Sonntag, "Halogenation, Dehalogenation, and De-hydrohalogenation," in Klare S. Markley, Ed., *Fatty Acids,* Part 2, 2nd Edition, Interscience Publishers, New York, 1961, pp. 1128 *ff.*
27. G. Egle, U.S. Patent 3,481,959 (1969).
28. Louis F. Fieser and Mary Fieser, *Topics in Organic Chemistry,* Reinhold Publishing Corporation, New York, 1963, p. 334.
29. D. E. Floyd, *Polyamide Resins,* 2nd Edition, Reinhold Publishing Corporation, New York, 1966, p. 11.
30. See Reference 29, p. 16.
31. L. B. Falkenburg, H. M. Teeter, P. S. Skell and J. C. Cowan, *Oil and Soap,* **22,** 143 (1945).
32. J. C. Cowan, L. B. Falkenburg, H. M. Teeter and P. S. Skell, U.S. Patent 2,450,940 (1948).
33. See Reference 29, pp. 50-52, 87-88.
34. M. M. Renfrew and H. Wittcoff, U.S. Patent 2,705,223 (1955).
35. See Reference 29, pp. 87-88.
36. D. W. Young and E. Lieber, U.S. Patent 2,411,178 (1946); W. J. Sparks and D. W. Young, U.S. Patent 2,424,588 (1947); D. W. Young and W. J. Sparks, U.S. Patent 2,435,619 (1948).
37. M. Rosenberg, U.S. Patent 3,492,232 (1970).
38. R. J. Sturwold and F. O. Barrett, U.S. Patent 3,769,215 (1973).
39. R. E. Layman, U.S. Patent 3,158,584 (1964).
40. M. T. O'Gorman and J. D. Downs, U.S. Patent 3,530,082 (1970).
41. A. J. Coury, U.S. Patent 3,549,570 (1970).
42. R. D. Aylesworth, R. H. Boehringer, D. T. Moore and M. H. Smith, *Modern Plastics,* **35,** 145 (1958).
43. R. J. Ferrari, J. W. Sinner, J. C. Bill and W. F. Brucksch, *Ind. Eng. Chem.,* **50,** 1041 (1958).
44. A. J. Coury and J. E. Wicklatz, U.S. Patent 3,493,534 (1970).
45. E. Earl Royals, *Advanced Organic Chemistry,* Prentice-Hall, Inc., New York, 1954, pp. 609-610.
46. L. R. Le Bras and R. E. Park, U.S. Patent 3,068,254 (1962).
47. J. J. Seiwert and J. B. Boylan, U.S. Patent 3,406,134 (1968).
48. D. Laganis, U.S. Patent 3,498,940 (1970).
49. C. Burba, M. Drawert and E. Griebsch, U.S. Patent 3,578,612 (1971).
50. L. R. Vertnik, U.S. Patent 3,217,028 (1965).
51. L. R. Vertnik, U.S. Patent 3,281,470 (1966).
52. R. Nordgren, L. R. Vertnik and H. Wittcoff, U.S. Patent

3,235,596 (1966).

53. L. R. Vertnik and H. Wittcoff, U.S. Patent 3,231,545 (1966); 3,242,141 (1966).

54. D. E. Peerman and L. R. Vertnik, U.S. Patent 3,483,237 (1969).

55. J. R. Nazy and K. B. Stokes, U.S. Patent 3,493,543 (1970).

56. W. C. Simpson, U.S. Patent 2,956,034 (1960).

57. H. A. Newey, U.S. Patent 2,940,986 (1960).

Commercial Applications of Dimer Acids and Their Derivatives

Lawrence A. Fury and Kenneth T. Mecklenborg—Humko
Sheffield Chemical, Memphis, Tennessee

Lawrence U. Berman and Melvin L. Loeb—Research and
Development, Kraftco Corporation, Glenview, Illinois

A. INTRODUCTION

The dimer acids derived from unsaturated C_{18} fatty acid feedstocks have several distinct features:

1. They are capable of reacting, like other unsaturated acids, at the carboxyl groups, at the site of unsaturation, and at the α-carbon, the first being most important commercially (see Chapter 3).

2. They are the highest molecular weight dibasic acid commercially available. The large aliphatic component imparts hydrophobicity to products using the dimer acids, e.g., corrosion inhibitors.

3. Polymers based on dimer acids lack crystallinity and tend to be flexible and have desirable low-temperature properties. These characteristics are a result, in part, of the complex composition of the acids.

These properties give the dimer acids a unique position among commercial dibasic acids and make them suitable for a myriad of end uses. This is evident from the technical literature, in which the number of references to the dimer acids and derivatives increases steadily each year.

This chapter is a presentation of the most important applications of the dimer acids and their derivatives. The presentation is not meant to be exhaustive, but is broad enough to give the reader lead references to pursue a topic and expand on it. The chapter has two major sections: 1) applications related to monomeric species of dimer and its derivatives, and 2) those applications involving polymeric species.

B. APPLICATIONS OF DIMER ACIDS

One of the earliest, most widely-used applications of dimer acids is for corrosion inhibition, especially in petroleum-processing equipment. The unique structure of dimer acids, with two polar carboxyl groups and a large non-polar hydrocarbon component, is the key to adsorption of the molecule to metals. The adsorbed complex gives a hydrophobic surface which protects against penetration by water and other polar agents. Dimer acids, by themselves (1, 2, 3), and in combination with other additives (4, 5, 6, 7, 8, 9, 10), have been used for this purpose. Formulations containing dimer acids are used to protect down-well parts in oil rigs against corrosion from agents such as CO_2, H_2S, and acetic acid (11, 12, 13, 14, 15). One part dimer acids and four parts of an ethoxylated polyamide is used as a corrosion-inhibitor composition for gasoline (16). Dimer acids and triisopropylamine serve as an effective corrosion inhibitor for polyglycol fluids (17). Other compositions containing dimer acids are claimed to protect copper-containing metals (18) and are used with hexavalent chromium-containing coating compositions (19). In antirust mineral oil formulations, dimer acids act as an emulsion-depressant in the presence of water (20).

In petroleum products, dimer acids have additional uses aside from corrosion inhibition. In jet fuels, they are reported as a stabilizer against thermal degradation (21, 22, 23). In gasoline they can act as a detergent, forming easily-removed granular deposits (24). In refined lubricant compositions, dimer acids are used as an antiwear agent (25, 26, 27) and as an extreme-pressure agent (28); they also serve synthetic lubricants in the latter application (29). A recent patent describes the use of dimer (and/or trimer) acids with an oleophilic clay as a gear lubricant with superior film retention properties (30). With arylcarbamyl grease thickeners, dimer acids improve the yield without decreasing performance (31). In bitumen asphalt, they produce a material which bonds more securely to a filler and is more resistant to weathering (32).

In the general area of lubrication, dimer acids are a stabilizer in cold-rolling oils for metals, functioning as a coolant as well as inhibiting degradation (33). With mineral oil, they act as a lubricant for the metal-mold interface in a continuous casting operation (34). Added to animal, vegetable, or mineral oils, dimer acids provide lubricity and cohesion to textile fibers during fabrication (35).

Applications for dimer acids in polymer technology are very broad. They harden epoxy resins, and also impart flexibility to the cured system (36, 37, 38). Automotive body solders are made from a curable, thixotropic composition consisting of diepoxides, dimer acids, a polycarboxylated anhydride, a silicate, a stannous acylate, and an onium cation-exchanged bentonite (39). Dimer dianhydrides from dimer acids and acetic anhydride act as curing agents for epoxy resins (40). Dimer acids can be incorporated during the polymerization of styrene to function as a processing lubricant in the finished product (41, 42). Nylon can be modified with dimer acids to improve the lubricity and to increase the wear life of the fibers (43). In the manufacture of polypropylene fibers, dimer acids can be dissolved in the melt for marked improvement in the uptake of basic, oil-soluble, and dispersed dyestuffs (44). Dimer acids serve as a lubricant for PVC sealing gaskets in jar twist caps (45). The acyl chlorides of dimer acids can be converted to the diketene, which is an effective reactive sizing agent for cellulosic fibers (46). An early patent (47) describes the use of dimer acids as a plasticizer for zein and other prolamines. An aqueous emulsion of dimer acids and a polyalkyleneimine can be cured on leather as an antiscuff agent (48).

In papermaking, dimer acids, incorporated in a binder dispersion, will aid uniform deposition of the binder onto the fibers (49). The wet strength of paper is improved when dimer acids are combined with tris(1-aziridinyl) phosphine oxide for impregnation (50). Similarly, the fiber in wall boards is stabilized when impregnated with dimer acids (51).

Dimer acids also have been employed in a number of miscellaneous applications. They are an effective aid in dispersing alkali metals in a hydrocarbon medium (52). They act as a stabilizer in winterizing vegetable oils (53); similarly, dimer acids and lanolin prevent precipitation in concentrated hydrocarbon solutions of DDT (54). Dimer acids are used in an enteric coating formulation for controlled dosage of a drug (55). They can be dissolved in a hydrocarbon oil, with other ingredients, and sprayed on coal to prevent degradation by dusting and to improve weathering (56). Aqueous amide-based deicers (e.g., urea-formamide) cause hydrogen embrittlement in steel, which results in failure in stress areas. The incorporation of dimer acids in these deicers markedly inhibits hydrogen embrittlement (57). Dimer (and/or trimer) acids—when mixed with a wax, light oil, and an emulsifier—form a film which effectively retards evaporation from large expanses of water (58). A similar concept has been suggested for hurricane control (59).

C. APPLICATIONS OF MONOMER ACIDS AND DERIVATIVES

Commercially, fractions from the dimerization reaction in the production of dimer acids are separated by molecular distillation. The lowest-boiling fraction consists of monobasic acids, composed of a minor amount of saturated and unsaturated straight chain acids and a major amount of branched-chain (iso) acids. The iso acids are both saturated and unsaturated and are the product of side-reactions occurring during dimerization. The mixture is designated as monomer acids (monomer). It was found that by hydrogenating the monomer and then separating the branched-chain acids, a unique fatty acid fraction was obtained (60). The saturated, branched-chain acids are liquid at room temperature, display many of the properties of oleic acid, but have oxidative and thermal stability similar to that of stearic acid. These branched-chain, saturated acids contain mostly 18 carbon atoms, hence are termed "Isostearic Acid," and have been described in previous chapters.

Although the monomer acids have certain commercial uses, the isostearic acid fraction is utilized in the main. The combined properties of liquidity and stability lead to interesting and varied applications, both for the acid itself and with its derivatives. Suggested broad areas of application are in cosmetics, detergents, emulsifiers, sanitary chemicals, lubricants, greases, textile chemicals, paper supplies, rubber, and plastics. More specific examples follow.

Isostearic acid forms amides with polyamines which furnish a superior ashless detergent lubricant composition having pour-point depressant properties (61, 62). Various bisamides of isostearic acid improve the adhesion of lubricants to metal surfaces (63). Isostearic acid, as the monoamide of N-2-hydroxyethyl-1,2-ethylenediamine, has been suggested as a gasoline detergent (64). Secondary amines prepared from the acid are oxidation inhibitors in synthetic lubricants (65). Esters from polyols and isostearic acid are synthetic lubricants with superior stability and lowered pour points (66). Pentaerythritol tetraisostearate can be a component of synthetic greases (67). The alkaline earth soaps of the acid are alkali reserve agents in lubricant compositions (68).

Derivatives of isostearic acid also find application in textiles. Alkali soaps of the acid and a synthetic detergent cleanse and soften the fabric (69). The diisostearyl dimethyl quaternary salt, and its analogs, are textile softeners (70, 71, 72).

In cosmetics, the partially neutralized acids in a shampoo formulation improve cleansing and conditioning of the hair, while aiding storage-separation stability of the product (73). In lipstick formulations, isostearyl alcohol acts as the oil phase imparting a wide range of plastic properties. It is also a good solvent for the dyes in the lipstick and its inherent stability eliminates the need for an antioxidant in these formulations (74). Several esters have been suggested as emollients in cosmetic formulations; these are the monoisostearic esters of glycerol, propylene glycol, and isopropanol (75).

Esters of isostearic acid and polyhydric alcohols (e.g., glycerol, propylene glycol) also are utilized as emulsifiers in frozen confections of the oil-in-water type. As such, they improve dryness and meltdown stability in ice milk (76). Isostearic acid stabilizes and controls the evaporation rate of dimethyl dichlorovinyl phosphate in insecticidal compositions (77). Aluminum powder coated with the acid shows little dusting during handling, thus enhancing safety and pollution control (78). Isostearic acid, when included in the magnetic layer of magnetic recording tape, improves resistance to abrasion and reduces corrosion (79). A mixture of the acid, a polysiloxane, and polyvinyl alcohol coated on heavy wrapping paper and cured with a tin compound, gives a paper which has excellent scratch resistance and is useful for packaging of items with polished surfaces (80). The isostearylamide of alpha-benzylbenzylamine (racemic, d-, or l-) is a cholesterol-lowering agent (81).

D. APPLICATIONS OF TRIMER ACIDS AND DERIVATIVES

In commercial or laboratory processes the fatty acid dimerization does not stop at a 36-carbon atom molecule, but proceeds to some extent to form trimeric and higher oligomeric acids. These acids are isolated as the molecular distillation residue and, lumped together, are called "Trimer Acids." Depending on distillation conditions, the distillation residue can contain up to 90% trimer acids.

Trimer acids possess high viscosities and refractive indices and, being a residue, are darker than monomer or dimer acids. Formulations containing trimer acids have physical properties distinct from the corresponding dimer acids formulations. As expected, for example, trimer acids cross-link when reacted with other polyfunctional molecules leading to high viscosity polymers and, eventually, gels. Gelling can be avoided, however, by inclusion of monocarboxylic acids to an average acid functionality of approximately two. Trimer acids can be combined with monomer acids to produce products having physical properties similar to those obtained from dimer acids. When trimer acids are used for a particular application the effect of the functionality of trimer versus dimer acids on the desired properties of the final products should be given full consideration.

Trimer acids are closely related to dimer acids and they, and their simple derivatives, possess properties similar to dimer acids. For this reason, many applications of trimer acids are also described in the applications literature of dimer acids. However, in certain applications trimer acids are preferred to dimer acids. This is particularly true for applications using the cross-linking properties of trimer acids. Examples of such applications are encapsulation, molding, and foamed polyurethanes.

Trimer acids are specified as a detergent in fuel compositions for spark-ignited internal combustion engines. The detergent is in the form of an ammonium salt-ethoxylated allylphenol ester mixture (82) and as simple esters, such as tris-(tridecyl) trimerate (83). In jet fuel compositions, antiwear agents have been based on trimer acids; trimer is used by itself (84) or in combination with a monoamine salt of a hydrogen dialkylphosphate (85).

Monoamides of heterocyclic amines and trimer acids are extreme-pressure and load-carrying additives for synthetic lubricants, especially the hindered ester type (86). Trimer acids improve the retention properties of a gear lubricant (determined by the Timken Retention Test) (30). An ester, tris(2-ethylhexyl) trimerate, is a component in a synthetic grease composition (67). Esters of trimer acids and hydroxy compounds (molecular weights greater than 400) are specified as demulsifiers in the water-in-oil emulsions found in oil wells and storage tanks (87). Small amounts of trimer acids are used to clarify used metalworking lubricant oils (88). A formulation of dimer/trimer acids in mineral oil, with sufficient glyceride to solubilize the trimer acids, is employed for lubrication of the metal-mold interface in a continuous casting operation (34). An ester of glycerol and trimer acids is incorporated in a bituminous material applied as a binder or potting compound (89). Trimer acids are preferred over dimer acids in a borated amide of N-alkyl alkylenediamine as a rust inhibitor in lubricating oils (90).

An alkali metal soap of trimer acids prepared *in situ* acts as a dispersant for aqueous emulsions. Materials which can be dispersed include oils, waxes, and particulate inorganic materials such as metal oxides (91). The potassium soap of trimer acids in water-laid sheets of asbestos improves sheet strength and decreases the drain time (92).

Polyethylene terephthalate and its copolyesters are made cationically dyeable by incorporating the reaction product of trimer acids and sodium isethionate (93). Trihydroxyethyl trimerate and bis(hydroxyethyl) dimerate, incorporated into a terephthalate polyester, gives staple fibers with good resistance to pilling and improved disperse dyeability (94). Trimer acids incorporated into polyolefins (polyethylene and polypropylene) aid flow resistance and inhibit the tendency to melt fracture (95). Polyesters made from mercapto acids, trimer acids, and polyhydroxy compounds are shrink- and wrinkle-resistant finishes for wool (96). A polyester made from trimer acids, thioglycolic acid, and a polypropylene glycol is a finishing agent for synthetic fibers (97). A nonlinear polyester resin, with enhanced flexibility for coatings, results from a mixture of phthalic acid and maleic acid, a mixture of a simple glycol and polyglycol, and trimer acids (98).

Trimer acids significantly improve the mechanical properties of the propellant and liner for solid propellant rocket motors (99). The reaction of trimer acids with a polyisocyanate in the presence of a catalyst produces a self-foaming, high-temperature-resistant polymer with fairly uniform cell structure. Suggested applications for this foamed polymer are liners for solid propellant motors, insulation, compressible gasketing, and paint applicators (100). Similarly, a prepolymer from a glycol ester of trimer (dimer) acids and toluene diisocyanate, cured with castor oil, forms a polyurethane fuel binder for a solid propellant (101).

Trimer acids are a flexibilizer for epoxy resins; the resulting cross-linked products are characterized by high tensile strength, good elasticity, and stability to heat and to solvents (102, 103). Curable coatings and sealing compositions are prepared from trimer acids, an asphalt, and an epoxy resin (e.g., glycidyl ethers of Bisphenol A). Such formulations are suggested for surfacing roads and airfields to improve weatherability, skid resistance, and solvent resistance (104, 105, 106). A similar composition emulsified in water with soap is used in bonding glass fiber into mats (107).

A novel application of trimer acids, mixed with mineral oil and a spreading agent, is the retardation of evaporation from large bodies of water (58).

E. APPLICATIONS OF LOW-MOLECULAR-WEIGHT DERIVATIVES OF DIMER ACIDS

1. *Applications of Dimer Soaps*

Dimer acids form soaps (salts) when neutralized with inorganic and organic bases. The soaps of dimer acids are more oleophilic than those of the C_{18} fatty acids. This property leads to a number of applications involving an affinity for hydrocarbon systems.

As is the case for many other derivatives of dimer acids, the soaps are used as corrosion or antirust inhibitors. Some are disclosed for use in oil wells, e.g., the dimer acids salt of 2-methylpiperazine (108), salts of the reaction product of an alkylene polyamine and dimer acids (109), amine salts (e.g., octylamine) of the ester of diphenolic acid and dimer acids (110), amine salts of the ester of triethanolamine and dimer acids (111), and amine salts of the monopentyl ester of dimer acids (112). Other inhibitors are imidazoline salts (113) and glyoxalidene salts (114, 115, 116). Sulfonates of dimer diamido diamines make up part of an anticorrosive mineral oil composition (117). Improved rust inhibition in a multifunctional lubricant can be obtained using dimer acids which have been partially neutralized with zinc oxide (118). Other anticorrosion compositions contain salts of dimer acids and a diamine, along with an ethoxylated alkyl phenol (119), or the reaction product of a diamine and epichlorohydrin (120). Dimer acids salts of a water-soluble amine together with a metal deactivator is used for corrosion protection in polyglycol fluids (17). Alkali metal soaps of dimer acids are used in glycol-water systems to impart rust protection (121). Dimer acids salts of 1-salicylalamino-guanidine have been found to be antioxidants and copper deactivators—especially for petroleum products (122). A metalworking lubricant composition contains alkanolamine salts of dimer acids to impart antirust properties (123).

The phosphate salt of an aminoalkylamide of dimer acids

acts as a lubricant coating for ferrous metals in a phosphating bath (124). The dimer acids salt of a condensation product of epichlorohydrin and a fatty amine stabilizes hydrocarbon oils in a heat exchanger (125). The salt of dimer acids and a dialkylaminopropyl amide acts as an anti-stalling agent in gasoline (126).

Soaps of dimer acids, analogously to the soaps of fatty acids, act as gelling agents in petroleum fractions. Aluminum soaps of dimer acids form improved greases or gels with liquid hydrocarbons (127, 128, 129, 130, 131, 132). Other soaps include sodium (133), lithium (134), calcium (135), and those of alkali and alkaline earth metals (136).

Soaps of dimer acids, in paint and coating formulations, act as pigment dispersants. Among the types used are ammoniated soaps (137, 138), alkali metal soaps (139), diethylenetriamine, morpholine and other amine salts (140, 141), and the salt of the condensate of an epichlorohydrin with an amine (142).

Soaps of Group IIb metals and dimer acids added to polyolefins improve the dye receptivity of dispersed dyes in textile fibers (143). Other soaps disclosed are those of copper, chromium, manganese, nickel, and cobalt (144). Polyester fibers are made cationically dyeable by incorporating three to seven weight percent of the sodium salt of dimer isethionate (93).

Trivalent metal soaps of dimer acids improve the drainage rate of a slurry of cellulosic fibers in the papermaking process (145). An analogous application is used in processing water-laid asbestos fibers (92). Soaps of dimer acids allow an increase in the amount of binder that can be added to cellulose and asbestos fibers (146). Amine salts of dimer acids make a coating of waxless carbon paper more oleophilic (147). Soluble salts used in blasting agents, delayed-action fertilizers, and dynamite mixtures are waterproofed by overlaying with a gelled hydrocarbon containing the aluminum soap of dimer acids (148). The colloid stability in the preparation of a high-solids chloroprene polymer latex is adequately maintained with the potassium soaps of dimer acids (149, 150).

The triethanolamine salt of dimer acids is disclosed as a "mildness additive" with various detergents. Reduced skin irritation is noted on laboratory test animals (151, 152, 153).

2. *Applications of Dimer Esters*

Dimer acids are readily esterified with alcohols under standard esterification conditions. This section deals with esters prepared from simple monofunctional alcohols, and higher esters prepared using an excess of difunctional alcohols (glycols). More complex derivatives of dimer acids, e.g., those incorporated in a polyester system such as alkyds and polyurethanes, will be discussed in a section to follow.

Esters of dimer acids have found use as lubricants and lubricant additives. For example, dibutyl dimerate and similar dialkyl esters are a base fluid component in a synthetic lubricant (154, 155, 156) and an anti-squawk agent in a transmission fluid (157). The diesters of dimer acids and oil-insoluble glycols in the range of 2-8 carbon atoms act as lubricity additives (158). Branched-chain primary aliphatic alcohol esters of dimer acids are detergents in multi-viscosity-grade lubricating-oil compositions (159). The bis(2-ethylhexyl) ester of dimer acids and diisodecyl azelate (3:1) blended with an additive mixture is a synthetic lubricant, with good detergent properties, useful in internal-combustion engines (160). The dimer acids ester of the condensation product of an alkyl amine and epichlorohydrin is recommended as a pour-point depressant for a hydrocarbon oil (125). The ethyl (2-thienyl) dimerate is suitable as a low-temperature lubricant, or lubricant additive (161). A number of alkyl esters are instrument lubricants, e.g., for watches and clocks (162). Two examples of metalworking lubricants capable of forming aqueous compositions have been reported. One is the ester of dimer acids and polyoxyethylene glycol (e.g., Carbowax 400) (163); the other is a mixture of the ester of dimer acids, a lower dibasic acid (e.g., azelaic), and polyoxyethylene glycol (164). An ester such as the product of dimer acids and sorbitan monooleate shows good load-carrying characteristics in a lubricant composition for machinery (165).

Esters of dimer acids combined with fatty acid lithium soaps form greases of superior quality (166). Compositions containing the esters of dimer acids and polyoxyethylene glycols display nonflammable properties (167). Esters having good low-temperature properties are made from polyoxypropylene glycols (168, 169). Benzyl and benzhydryl esters of dimer acids are useful in lubricants and in hydraulic fluids (170).

Esters of dimer acids are useful as surface-active agents. Esters derived from dimer acids and polyethylene oxide are nonionic surface-active agents and are used as emulsifiers for synthetic resins in the dyeing of metalized fabrics (171, 172).

Similar disclosures are found in other references (173). The partial ester of phthalic anhydride and the dimer acids of 9, 11-linoleyldiricinolein is a demulsifier for breaking petroleum emulsions (174). The condensation product of dimer acids with a low-molecular-weight polyalkylene oxide, added to a mono- or dialkylolamine, is used to impart antistatic properties to textile fibers (175). A polysaccharide ester of dimer acids and a fatty acid improves resistance to deposition of high melting solids in salad oils (176). Dimer esters of 3,3,5,5 -tetrakis(hydroxymethyl)-4-hydroxytetrahydropyran display the same property (177). The ester drived from the acidolysis of glycerides with dimer and/or trimer acids is a crystal modifier which improves the solvent separation of saturated fatty acids from unsaturated fatty acids (178).

Esters of dimer acids are useful as corrosion or rust inhibitors. The lauryl ester of the condensation product of dimer acids and maleic acid imparts corrosion-inhibition properties to mineral oil compositions (179). Another type is the partial ester of dimer acids and a hydroxyaliphatic cyclic amidine (180). Esters of 1,4-butanediol are good corrosion inhibitors for petroleum hydrocarbons because they form no gum and are ashless (181). The ester of dimer acids and triethanolamine is used as a corrosion inhibitor in oil wells (182). Esters such as those obtained from sorbitan monooleate and dimer acids are compounded into turbine oils to prevent rusting and corrosion of metal parts (183, 184).

Dimer esters act as coreactants in certain polymerizations, leading to a flexible polymer. Dimethyl dimerate is used in polyesters (185), in polyamides (186, 187), and in the esterification of resins to produce epoxy esters (188). The ester of ethylene glycol and dimer acids can act as a coreactant in making terephthalate polyester resin. Fibers prepared from this kind of resin have improved affinity for dyes (189, 190). A different sort of polymer application is found in the use of tetrahydrofurfuryl dimerate as a polyvinyl chloride plasticizer (191). In a similar application, dialkyl esters of dimer acids such as the diethyl ester are reacted with dialkyl fumarates to produce adducts useful as polyvinyl chloride plasticizers (192).

3. *Applications of Dimer Amides*

In many instances, different derivatives of dimer acids have similar applications. The simple amides and the products of the reaction of dimer acids with monofunctional amines fall into this class, finding use as corrosion and rust inhibitors. As an example, the amides of various substituted piperazines and dimer acids are effective for inhibiting corrosion in oil well equipment (193). The amides of dimer acids and a polyalkylene amine, such as diethylenetriamine (194), and the co-amides of boric acid or its esters, are used in the same application (195). Other anticorrosion agents are the monoamides from primary or secondary amines and dimer acids (196), and the alkylthiophosphoric salts of the amide of dimer acids and polyalkylene amines (197).

The amide-ester of ethanolamine, stearic and dimer acids is used as a synthetic wax with properties similar to carnauba wax (198). A grease-thickening agent, useful at high temperatures (500°F), is prepared from 1.5 moles of dimer acids and 1.0 mole of n-hexadecylamine; the excess acid is neutralized with lithium hydroxide (199). The half amide of hydrogenated dimer acids, combined in a synthetic ester lubricant, acts as an antiscuff and antifatigue agent (200). Amidoamines from polyalkylene amines and dimer acids improve lubricity and act as an antiscuff agent for lubricating oils (201). Lower alkylene diamines and dimer acids give amides useful as antiwear additives for lubricating oils (202).

The piperidide of dimer acids is recommended as a primary solvent-type plasticizer for polyvinyl chloride resin (203), as are the morpholides of dimer acids (204, 205). Other PVC plasticizers disclosed are the N,N',N'-tetraalkyl diamides of dimer acids, such as the tetramethyl and tetraisopropyl derivatives (206), and the bis(2-alkoxyethyl) diamide (207). The condensation product of an epoxy resin and dimer acids, partially amidated with secondary amines such as piperazine and N-butylethanolamine, and cured with a dihydrazide, produces an adhesive with good electrical properties (208). Monoisocyanates react with dimer acids to produce amides, which then can be combined with an alkyd resin to give a thixotropic composition (209). The reaction product of dimer acids and an aliphatic amine makes up part of a sealant for plug valves (210). A temporary, heat-activated, pressure-sensitive adhesive is made from dimer acids and an alkanolamine (211). Alkanolamides of dimer acids can be reacted with various polyisocyanates to produce air-cured polyurethanes which form hard, tough coatings (212, 213, 214, 215). Foamed-in-place polyurethanes having excellent resistance to hydrolysis are made by reacting the alkanolamides of dimer acids and ethanolamine with a diisocyanate (216).

The alkylene oxide condensates of the alkanolamides of dimer acids are nonionic surface-active agents with good dispersing and emulsifying properties. These can be used as textile-dyeing assistants (217, 218). The alkanolamides are intermediates for the production of nonionic surface-active agents (219). The bis (p-hydroxyaryl) amides of dimer acids are useful as stabilizers in natural and synthetic rubbers (220). Derivatives of dimer acids, such as the alkanolamides, improve fuel emulsion stability (221). The diethanolamides and the morpholides of dimer acids (152), as well as the amide of dimer diprimary amine and caproic acid (153), are used as mildness additives to prevent skin irritation. Disulfides obtained by the oxidation of the dimer acids amide of 2-aminoethyl mercaptan have been reported (222).

4. *Applications of Dimer Glycol*

High-pressure hydrogenation of dimer acids (esters) using a copper-based catalyst yields a dialcohol variously referred to as dimer glycol, dimer alcohol, and dimer diol (223, 224). As a high-molecular-weight diol, it can be substituted into polyester and other polymer formulations as a modifier to promote flexibility.

With polyterephthalate systems, dimer glycol produces high-melting copolyesters which have high elongation and excellent elastic recovery (225, 226). Polyesters of dimer glycol and alpha, beta-unsaturated diacids are copolymerized with olefins, such as styrene, to give an elastic product suitable for floor coverings (227). With ethyl chloroformate, dimer diol is converted to a carbonate which can be condensed at elevated temperatures to yield polycarbonates suitable for cast films and adhesives (228). Reaction of polyisocyanates with dimer glycol and with ethoxylated dimer diol yields polyurethane lacquers which have good resistance to hydrolysis (229). Polyesters prepared from dimer diol with ethylene glycol, glycerine, and dimethyl terephthalate are utilized in coating formulations. They have a high degree of flexibility and heat stability. A typical application is the dipping of electrical windings (230). Sulfur-containing polyurethanes based on dimer diol produce highly elastic coatings. A polyisocyanate prepolymer is prepared from excess diisocyanate and dimer diol. The prepolymer is then reacted with the thioether of dimer diol and a thioglycol using an amine catalyst (231).

Unsaturated polyester resins used in filling and sealing compositions are made from dimer diol and fumaric acid, extended with maleic anhydride, and cured with peroxide after addition of styrene (232). Dimer diol is incorporated into a cellulose acetate butyrate formulation to give dipmolding, strippable coating compositions (233).

Water-in-oil emulsions can be prepared using dimer diol as an emulsifier (234). Glycidyl ethers used as adhesives and primers are made from dimer diol and epichlorohydrin (235). Incorporation of 0.1 to 5 percent dimer diol into styrene prior to polymerization imparts lubricity to the polymer (236). In detergent compositions containing alkylbenzene sulfonates or sodium lauryl sulfate, dimer glycol inhibits skin irritation and is termed a mildness additive (152). Esters of the glycol, including the ester of dimer acids and dimer glycol, also act as mildness additives (153).

5. Applications of Dimer Diprimary Amine and Dimer Diisocyanate

The diprimary amine of dimer acids (dimer diamine) is prepared commercially through the ammonolysis of the acid to the dinitrile, followed by reduction of the dinitrile to the diamine (237). The dimer amine has the chemical properties of a typical diamine.

Dimer diprimary amine is utilized in a number of polymer systems. For example, cycloaliphatic and aliphatic dibasic acids react with dimer diamine, mixed with a short-chain diamine, to give polyamides useful as casting resins, surface coatings, and adhesive materials (238). A similar system uses aromatic compounds such as isophthalic and terephthalic acids (239). With 6-aminocaproic acid the diamine is converted to an amine-terminated polyamide which can be reacted to polyamideureas useful as molding compounds (240, 241). Dimer diamine, with a second diamine, reacts with dimer acids and a second dibasic acid to give a series of novel polyamide resins (242). The condensation product of dimer diamine with another diamine and tetracarboxylic acids, such as pyromellitic acid, is useful for electrical insulation (243).

Dimer diamine reacts with phosgene to yield a dimer diisocyanate. The diisocyanate can be used to pretreat wood to prevent cracking and darkening of resin varnishes (244). Polyureas can be made from dimer diisocyanate and a diamine. Dimer diisocyanate and diethylenetriamine gives a reactive polyurea which is capable of forming a self-curing film with epoxy resins (245). The diisocyanate is cured with a ketimine and extended with a petroleum oil to give polyurea coatings which have outstanding weathering properties (246).

Another method of preparing polyureas is to react dimer diamine and urea or thiourea (247). Dimer diisocyanate, blocked with oximes, is used to treat paper or leather which, upon heat treatment, regenerates the diisocyanate. This reacts to modify the surface to give water repellency (248).

Paper fibers can be made water repellent with dimer diisocyanate and a quaternary ammonium polygalactomannan gum ether as a cationic retention agent (249). The dimensional stability of wood to moisture is improved by impregnation with a mixture of dimer diisocyanate and dimer diisocyanate reacted with a ketimine-blocked polyamine such as diethylenetriamine (250). Metal substrates are protected by chip-resistant coatings of dimer diisocyanate and ketimine-blocked polyamines followed by a heat-curable acrylic coating (251). Soil release and softness of textiles are improved by treatment with a urethane-capped diisocyanate based on dimer diisocyanate and a polyglycol. The free isocyanate groups can be blocked by oximes before curing (252). Isocyanurate elastomers, useful as gaskets or for coatings, are prepared from dimer diisocyanate in the presence of an amine-alkylene oxide ionic polymerization catalyst such as triethylenediamine and styrene oxide (253). Modified glycidyl isocyanurates, useful in the preparation of mastics and coatings, are prepared by treating a triglycidyl isocyanurate with dimer diisocyanate. The product is molded and cured with an anhydride (254).

Dimer diamine can act as a mold-release agent for nylons, especially polycaprolactam (0.25 pts to 10.0 pts) (255). The diisocyanate has also been used for this purpose (256). Dimer diamine dihydrochloride with montmorillonite clay increases the retention of anionic dyes on cellulosic fibers (257). The fatty acid salts of dimer diamine are useful as corrosion inhibitors for ferrous metals in the presence of oil and aqueous phases (258). Several dimer derivatives, of which dimer diamine is one, are utilized as emulsion stabilizers for hydrocarbon fuel emulsions (221). The capric acid salt of dimer diamine can be used as a mildness additive in cationic detergents (152, 153).

6. *Applications of Other Simple Nitrogen Derivatives of Dimer Acids*

Many other nitrogen derivatives of dimer acids have found practical applications. Ditertiary amines, tetraalkyl dimer diamines, are antistatic additives and antioxidants for plastics, especially polyethylene. They are made by reducing the amides of dialkyl amines and dimer acids (259). Hydrogenation of the cyanoethylation product of dimer diamine and acrylonitrile yields a tetramine, a bis(aminopropyl) amine, which is useful as a corrosion inhibitor for ferrous metals in contact with aqueous hydrogen sulfide (260).

Reaction of dimer diamine with methyl chloride yields a quaternary salt which is useful as a paper softener (261). Benzyl trialkyl ammonium halides react with the sodium soap of dimer acids to give quaternaries having bactericidal activity (262). Similarly, quaternization of the aminopropylamine derivative of dimer acids with methyl chloride yields a salt having bactericidal activity (263).

Dimer acids react with polyamines to yield imidazoline derivatives which are the basis of compositions used to prevent corrosion in oil wells in contact with "sweet" or "sour" petroliferous fluids (264). Ethylene oxide adducts of dimer acids imidazoline derivatives have been proposed for the same application (265). Other derivatives of dimer acids having corrosion-inhibiting properties include imidazolines and tetrahydropyrimidines containing free carboxyl groups (266), diurethane derivatives (267), and imidazolines treated with sulfur trioxide (268). Sulfonated tetrahydropyrimidines and imidazolines from dimer acids are useful for inhibiting sludge formation in fuel oil (269).

Substituted salts of dimer acids imidazolines protect metals against corrosion caused by the decomposition of halogenated organic insecticides in hydrocarbon solution (270). A bisoxazoline compound formed from dimer acids and ethanolamine followed by reaction with phosphorous pentasulfide has been found to inhibit corrosion in oil-producing equipment (271). Dimer dinitrile prepared by the ammonolysis of dimer acids can be treated with dicyandiamide to form a guanamine. Another route is through the reaction of biguanide and an ester of dimer acids. These guanamines are strongly basic and act as coreactant curing agents with epoxy resins. For example, the guanamines and diglycidyl ethers of polyalkylene glycols form adhesives. These can be partially cured for commercial handling and then finally cured to give a hard thermosetting bond (272, 273). This process can be extended by applying the partially cured resin as a powder on metal articles in a fluidized bed. Again, final curing gives a strong thermosetting coating (274). The same curing cycle can be carried out on fibrous materials, after impregnation, to form laminates (275). A partially cured resin can also be made from dimer acids-derived guanamine and epoxidized phenol-formaldehyde condensate (276, 277). Dimer guanamines form resins with formaldehyde which can be incorporated into coating compositions containing drying oils (278).

F. APPLICATIONS OF HIGH-MOLECULAR-WEIGHT DIMER ACIDS DERIVATIVES

1. *Applications of the Polyesters of Dimer Acids*

The value of dimer acids polyesters as resins was first recognized (279, 280, 281) at the Northern Regional Laboratories of the United States Department of Agriculture. It was found that the reaction of dimer acids esters (and, in certain cases, the free acids) with glycols gave linear polyesters which could be vulcanized to rubber-like products. Apparently as a result of this work (282), polyesters were prepared from dimer acids and dimer glycol which were high-molecular-weight, low-melting resins. Some of these polyesters have properties similar to crude rubber and others are useful as plasticizers and blending agents in various plastics and rubber substitutes. The polyesters prepared from highly branched glycols (283) are thermoplastic polymers which can be employed in thermographic copy supplies for duplicating processes. Elastomeric resins (284) can be made from the copolyesters of dimer acids and aromatic dicarboxylic acids with glycols. Also, improved fibers are melt-spun from these types of copolyesters (189, 190, 285, 286, 287, 288, 289). It was found (290) that superior mechanical and elastic characteristics are obtained in resins prepared by polycondensation of propylene glycol with dimer acid and maleic anhydride. Resin can coatings (291) are manufactured by condensation of cyclopentadiene with dimer acid/maleic anhydride copolyesters. The resulting resins are fire-retardant if hexahalocyclopentadiene (292) is used instead of the nonhalogenated cyclopentadiene, or if a copolyester with a perchlorobicyclic dicarboxylic acid is prepared and then dissolved in styrene (293). Polymers cross-linkable by moisture, useful as coatings, sealants, and adhesives, are prepared from the copolyester of bis(hydroxyethyl) dimer/maleic anhydride, a polyfunctional nitrile N-oxide-forming compound, and an inorganic base (294). Organosols, useful as coatings, plasticizers and adhesives are obtained by solution copolymerization of a vinyl monomer with the copolyester of dimer acids and maleic anhydride (295).

Copolymers of the diallyl esters of dimer acids and of phthalic acid are used to give infusible coatings (296). An unusual resin which forms films with increased flexibility and adhesion, from "which the vinyl groups do not escape," is made from dimer acids and an amine-containing polyol (297). The polyester is heated to form a polyester-oxazoline and then reacted with maleic anhydride to obtain the vinyl groups. Dimer polyesters are used in compounding dienenitrile and dienenitrile-polyvinyl chloride rubbers (298). A synthetic drying oil with superior properties results from the dimer acids polyester of an oxalkylated phenol-formaldehyde condensate (299). Various glycol polyesters of dimer acids are useful as plasticizers (300). Copolyesters of dimer acids, aromatic and aliphatic acids are claimed to improve the washfast finish and body of textiles (301, 302). Copolyesters of dimer acids and isophthalic acid with various branched-chain diols are especially useful for bent metal coil coatings (303). Addition of aliphatic acids into the copolyester formulation produces resins useful as surface coatings and in paints (304). Improved thermal stability is claimed for the resin obtained by cross-linking unsaturated dimer copolyesters with vinyl monomeric cross-linking agents (305). Copolycarbonates prepared from dimer acids polyesters can be used as molded articles, as flexible packaging materials, and as adhesives (306). A linoleum adhesive is prepared from the polyester of dimer acids and pentaerythritol (307). Dimer acids polyesters also are used for non-drying, stretchable, general-purpose laminating adhesives (308) and for laminating composite mica insulation (309). Dimer acids polyesters are used in various types of hot-melt adhesive formulations (310, 311, 312). Tin salts are suggested for the rapid preparation of low-molecular-weight polyesters, which may be used as plasticizers or lubricant additives (313).

Certain dimer acids polyesters are synthetic lubricants with good aqueous emulsifying properties (164); others have water solubility (163) useful in metalworking. Polyesters of dimer acids are used principally as additives in lubricating oils. Thus, certain polyesters add detergency (314, 315), while others impart antiwear properties (316, 317, 318, 319, 320). Viscosity-index (V.I.) improvers can be prepared from dimer acids polyesters (321, 322). Certain dimer acids polyesters are both V.I. improvers and pour-point depressants (323, 324). Sulfurized polyesters (325) and copolyesters with alkitolanhydrides (326) are corrosion inhibitors in lubricating oils.

Dimer acids polyesters of hydroxyaliphatic cyclic amidine compounds (327) and combination copolyesters-copolyamides of dimer acids and resin or fatty acids (328) are corrosion inhibitors for aqueous systems (e.g., oil-well brines).

A polyester from dimer acids and a combination of glycols and polyethylene glycol is useful as a detergent for lubricating and fuel oils (329). The acid obtained by reaction of dimer acids-glycol polyesters with rosin is useful as a dispersant for synthetic rubber in water (330). Various types of dimer acids polyesters (331, 332, 333) and polyesteramide or amines (334, 335) are useful in breaking water-in-oil emulsions. A mixture in which one component is a polyester of dimer acids is reputed to be an antistatic agent for textiles (336). Both dimer and trimer acids polyesters are utilized as softening agents (textile assistants); a triol is employed for the former, while a diol is recommended for the latter polyester (337).

Polyesters based on dimer acids are common intermediates in the manufacture of alkyd resins (338, 339, 340, 341, 342, 343, 344, 345, 346). Alkyd resins incorporating dimer acids polyesters have found a number of unusual applications: to saturate felt for linoleum manufacture (347, 348), to coat paper (349), and to wet nylon in order to improve the affinity for hydrophobic coating materials (350). Other variations of the alkyd resin formulations make use of the polyesters of dimer acids and polyhydric phenols (351).

Polyesters of dimer acids play a large role as additives for polyurethane polymers, which are used as solid coatings, binders, and foamed (cellular) materials. Boylan (352), in 1966, discussed dimer acids-modified polyesters for use in polyurethane coatings. The dimer acids polyesters (353) or copolyesters (354) are used in coatings. Copolyesters of dimer or trimer acids (355) are used in polyurethanes where good mechanical and electrical properties are needed. Air-drying (356) and moisture-curable (357) polyurethane coatings are prepared using dimer acids polyesters. Dimer-trimer polyester-modified polyurethanes can be used for solid-propellant fuel binders (358, 101).

The major application of dimer acids polyesters for polyurethanes is in foamed, or cellular, materials. In 1958 (359), the dimer acids polyesters were described as intermediates for polyurethane foams. At about the same time, it was found (360) that dimer acids polyesters gave the most durable foams for stability towards humidity aging. It is reputed that the presence of trimer acids polyesters (100) insures a tougher foam. It is not surprising that various polyesters and copolyesters of dimer acids are employed in manufacturing many kinds of foamed polyurethane materials (361, 362, 363, 364, 365, 366, 367, 368, 369, 370).

There are many examples of dimer acids polyesters as components in epoxy resin formulations. In certain cases the acids themselves are used to form the polyester *in situ,* thereby curing or polymerizing the monomeric components. Examples of this type (371, 372, 373) are resins specifically formulated for hard, durable, chemically-resistant coatings (374), for flexible sealants with longer pot life (375), for laminates for the electronic and electrical industries (376), for solid propellant compositions (377), and for oil-in-water emulsions (378). In many cases, the dimer polyester is reacted with epoxy-containing compounds or the dimer ester itself contains epoxy groups. An epoxy resin with a multiplicity of applications is made from an epoxy ester of epoxidized dimer acids and epoxy-containing alcohols (379); the esters are used as stabilizers and plasticizers for halogen-containing polymers and as lubricants and softening agents for textiles. When cured within fabrics they tend to impart improved crease- and shrink-resistance. Epoxy resins with good dielectric properties are prepared from dimer acids polyesters (380, 381, 382). Polyesters based on hydrogenated dimer acids are used for epoxy molding resins to improve dimensional stability (383, 384, 385). Dimer acids and their polyesters are used to improve weatherability and durability of asphalt and concrete road surfaces (386, 387, 388, 389).

Dimer acids and their polyesters are useful in many coatings applications. For example, a glycidyl polyether polyphenol ester of dimer acids is used specifically as a traffic paint (390, 391). Certain copolyesters of dimer acids form water-dilutable epoxy coating resins (392, 393). Dimer glycidyl esters also are used in an epoxy formulation of a thermosetting powder for coating articles by the fluidized-bed method (394). Glycidyl esters, esterpolyethers, and copolyesters of dimer acids are used in various other epoxy coating resins (395, 396, 397, 398, 399). A review of the applications of dimer acids in various types of surface coatings was published in 1972 (400).

2. *Applications of Polyamides Based on Dimer Acids*

The use of dimer acids in the manufacture of polyamide resins is by far the most important of their many commercial applications. More than 50% of the total annual volume of dimer acids production is consumed in the manufacture of polyamide resin.

Many patents and review articles describe the manufacture and application of specifically-formulated polyamide resins, but the very first patents issued on dimer acids-based polyamides showed a surprisingly comprehensive understanding of the overall system (401, 402).

Polyamide resins can be prepared from dimer acids and trimer acids, or their amide-forming derivatives such as esters, anhydrides, or acyl halides, by condensation with a large variety of diamines, including aliphatic and aromatic diamines, heterocyclic diamines, and polyamines. Ethylenediamine yields a polyamide having a melting range of 90-110°C. Most dimer acids-based polyamide resins from other diamines melt at a lower range.

Dimer and trimer acids mixed with shorter-chain dibasic acids form polyamides generally having a higher melting range, depending on the amount of short-chain dibasic acid used.

Various monofunctional reactants can be used to modify the properties of the polyamide resins, including monofunctional alcohols, amines, acids, amino acids, and hydroxy acids. The modifiers are useful in changing physical properties such as gel tendencies, viscosity, and solubility characteristics. An excellent review of the early work on polyamides was published in 1945 (403).

The commercial production of polyamide resins based on dimer acids started in 1949 (401). Since then the volume of polyamide manufacture based on dimer acids has increased substantially. Production was reported to be 32 million pounds in 1972 and forecasts are as high as 45 million pounds for 1978. There were thirteen producers of dimer acids-based polyamides in the United States in 1972 (404).

Most of the polyamide resins based on dimer acids currently produced commercially fall into two categories: nonreactive or neutral polyamides, and reactive polyamides. The neutral polyamides are prepared from difunctional amines. Their physical properties range from sharp-melting solids to nonviscous liquids. The major applications of neutral polyamides are as hot-melt adhesives, printing-ink resins, and surface coatings. The reactive polyamides, prepared from polyfunctional amines, are usually nonviscous liquids. Important applications of the reactive polyamides are in the formation

of thermosetting resins by coreaction with epoxy or phenolic resins, for use as thermosetting surface coatings, structural adhesives, thermosetting adhesives, and potting and
casting resins.

In addition to becoming a part of the backbone of polyamide resins, dimer acids add desirable ancillary properties
to the resin, including flexibility, corrosion resistance, chemical resistance, adhesion, and imperviousness to moisture.

   a. *Applications of Neutral Polyamide Resins*
      I. *Printing Inks*

Dimer acids-based polyamide resins are widely used as the
resin binder in flexographic printing inks. Flexographic
printing is a form of letterpress printing, in which the ink is
applied to the surface to be printed by means of a flexible
rotating rubber mat. Polyamide resins are especially well
suited for flexographic printing on plastic films and metallic
foil laminates because the resins adhere very well to the
printed surface, they can be formulated to give a printed
surface with high gloss, and the ink does not crack if the
printed film is bent or deformed. The polyamide resins also
can be formulated to have good solubility in solvents which do
not attack the rubber flexographic printing roll.

Polyamides prepared by reacting dimer acids with
ethylenediamine have many of the properties required for
making suitable flexographic printing inks (401, 405). Without modification, however, these resins are soluble only in
aromatic and aliphatic hydrocarbon solvents which attack the
rubber mats. Resins with improved solubilities in blends of
hydrocarbons and alcohols such as ethanol and isopropanol
have been prepared by reacting mixtures of dimer acids and
dimerized rosin acids with ethylenediamine and hexamethylenediamine, modified with monofunctional reactants
such as fatty acids (406). A mixture of a polyamide resin and
a toluenesulfonamide-formaldehyde resin, soluble in *n*-
propanol, was also an early suitable flexographic printing ink
resin (407). Other polyamide resins soluble in mixtures of alcohols and hydrocarbons have been suggested for this use
(408, 409).

The preferred solvents for flexographic printing inks are
low-molecular-weight alcohols, especially ethanol, *n*-pro-
panol and isopropanol. These alcohols do not attack the rubber mats and they evaporate rapidly allowing suitable high-
speed printing.

Mixtures of dimer acids and lower-molecular-weight dibasic acids or anhydrides produces polyamides having higher alcohol solubility. Suitable dibasic acids or anhydrides include succinic anhydride, phthalic anhydride, tetrahydrophthalic anhydride, and dodecenylsuccinic anhydride (410). Diglycolic acid or its esters are also suitable for this purpose (411), as are styrene-methyl methacrylate copolymers (412), and spiroacetal dicarboxylic acids and esters (413).

The alcohol solubility of polyamides can also be improved by the use of various diamines or polyols, in addition to ethylenediamine. Examples include isophorone diamine, N,N,N′-trimethylhexamethylenediamine (414), propylenediamine, 4,4′-diaminodicyclohexylmethane (415), trimethylolpropane, other polyols, and hydroxylamines (416, 417). Cyclic lactams such as η-caprolactam (418) and ether diamines (419) may also be used.

Monofunctional molecules can be incorporated into the polyamide resins both to control the extent of cross-linking caused by trimer acids in the dimer acids and to increase the alcohol solubility of the resin. A variety of monofunctional reactants have been used including hydroxy acids such as glycolic acid, lactic acid, beta-hydroxypropionic acid, alpha-hydroxy-n-caproic acid, salicylic acid, and phenylacetic acid (420, 421), as well as short-chain acids such as acetic acid (422), formic acid, propionic acid, butyric acid (423), 2-ethylhexanoic acid (424, 425, 426), and itaconic acid (427). Other monofunctional reactants which may be used include 3-methoxypropylamine (428), diphenolic acid, para-hydroxybenzoic acid, and monobasic acids containing phenolic hydroxyl groups (429).

Dimer acids-based polyamide resins having good alcohol solubility and improved freeze-thaw properties recently have been described (430). A good description also is given of the requirements for flexographic printing inks based on dimer acids.

Recently, polyamide resins suitable for use in flexographic printing have been developed in which water can be used in conjunction with alcohols as the solvent (431, 432). Water is a preferred solvent since it is cheap, is readily available, is non-flammable, and does not pollute.

II. *Hot-Melt Adhesives*

Hot-melt adhesives are thermoplastic resins which have fairly sharp melting points. They are particularly useful in high-speed assembly operations such as packaging, can assembly, bookbinding, and shoe assembly. This usefulness is due to their ability to be applied in liquid form, eliminating the need for solvents. Adhesion occurs almost immediately upon application and, upon cooling below the solidification point of the resin, a strong adhesive bond forms.

There are a large number of commercially available hot-melt adhesive systems. The dimer acids-based polyamide resins are limited to specialized uses requiring high-performance adhesives. The major application for the dimer acids-based polyamide hot-melt adhesives is in the shoe industry where their excellent adhesion allows the bonding of shoe soles to uppers without the necessity of stitching with thread. Other uses are in the bonding of metals, such as side-seam cements in the formation of cans, eliminating the need for welding, and in the laminating of various plastic and metal films and foils.

Dimer acids-based polyamide resins suitable for use as hot-melt adhesives are similar to those used for flexographic printing inks. Since solvents are not used, however, the resins are formulated more specifically to obtain sharp-melting solids. Resins with outstanding adhesion, excellent flexibility, and resistance to wear can be formulated using mixtures of dimer acids and short-chain dibasic acids which influence the melting point.

Polyamides suitable for hot-melt bonding of metals can be prepared by reacting mixtures of dimer acids and other short-chain dibasic acids with mixtures of alkylenediamines containing 2-6 carbon atoms and polyalkylenepolyamines containing 3-5 amino groups (433). Short-chain dibasic acids suitable for use include glutaric acid, adipic acid, pimelic acid, suberic acid, azelaic acid, and sebacic acid, as well as phthalic and terephthalic acids. Typical diamines include ethylenediamine, propylenediamine, and hexamethylenediamine. Typical polyamines include diethylenetriamine, triethylenetetramine, and higher polyamines. Depending on the choice of reactants, thermoplastic resins with melting points ranging from 60°C to 170°C have been prepared.

Blends of polyamides are also effective. A resin adhesive having superior melt stability has been prepared by blending the melts of a mixture of purely dimer acids-based polyamide and a polyamide prepared from both dimer acids and short-chain dibasic acids (434).

Polyamide adhesives suitable for use as replacements for metal can solders (435), for cardboard food cartons (436), for heat-activated adhesive tapes (437), and many other adhesive uses have been prepared from dimer acids and other dibasic acids using a variety of diamines (438, 439, 440, 441). Hot-melt adhesives based on dimer acids have been prepared in a variety of different ways. Low-melting polyamide resins with excellent adhesive properties were prepared using frac-tionated dimer acids (>83% dimer acid content), and a mix-ture of ethylenediamine and 1,3-diaminopropane (442, 443), with sufficient monobasic acid present to counteract the effects of higher polymeric acids present in the dimer acids. As the purity of the dimer acids increased, the ratio of monomer to trimer required lessened rapidly. Polyamides with improved oxidation stability and, therefore, greater pot life, have been prepared from hydrogenated dimer acids together with an oxidation inhibitor (444).

Specific examples of other dibasic acids used with dimer acids to produce improved hot-melt adhesives include adipic acid, azelaic acid, sebacic acid (445, 446), aromatic dicar-boxylic acids (447), and oxidized olefins (448). Omega-amino-carboxylic acids and cyclic lactams may also be used (449, 450).

A variety of amines can also be used to give specific im-provements in the polyamides. Mixtures of diamines and ether diamines (451), aliphatic diamines containing 4-12 car-bons (452), polyoxalkyleneamines (453), alkanolamines (454), branched-chain diamines (455), cycloaliphatic diamines (456, 457, 458), heterocyclic diamines such as piperazine (459) and aromatic diamines (460) have all been used. The diamine prepared from dimer acids also has been used (242).

Various other reactants have been used to modify the polyamide resins, including aromatic hydroxy-containing compounds such as phenol, naphthol, 4,4'-dihydroxy-diphenyl, and resorcinol (461); diphenolic acid (462); and a variety of monofunctional alcohols, acids and amines.

Hot-melt adhesives from polyamides based on dimer acids can be supplied as flakes, pellets, blocks, and coils, for use either by simply melting in a pot or by using specialized hot-melt applicators. The modern industrial requirements for high-speed manufacturing and assembly has created a substantial market for hot-melt adhesives, and in those specialized applications where high-performance adhesives are required, such as shoe adhesives and can cements, dimer acids-based polyamides are widely used.

III. *Other Applications of Neutral Polyamides*

The properties which make neutral dimer acids-based polyamides useful in printing-ink resins and hot-melt adhe-sives are utilized in a variety of other commercial applications.

Polyamides formed by reacting dimer acids with an excess

of polyamines have been found to impart increased durability and rust protection when used as a component of coatings for metal surfaces (463). A lacquer suitable for coating electrical wiring was prepared in a similar fashion (464). Polyamides prepared from dimer acids, other dicarboxylic acids, monobasic fatty acids, and a variety of diamines have good peel strength and are useful in coatings on steel and plastics (465). Coatings suitable for use on cellulose films have been prepared using cellulose nitrate, a plasticizer, and a polyamide resin (466). Flame-retardant paints have been prepared using polyamide resins as one of the ingredients. Both intumescent coatings (467) and coatings containing flame-retardant additives (468) have been suggested, with polyamides based on dimer acids in the formulations.

Polyamides derived from dimer acids and various polyamines adhere to a variety of substances, such as paper, plastics, and metals (469). Materials coated with these resins are impervious to air, moisture, and grease, and are suitable for use in packaging. Similar coatings with excellent heat-seal properties have also been developed (470, 471, 472). Other coatings suitable for packaging applications have been prepared from dimer acids and specific ether diamines (473) as one of the ingredients. Hydrocarbon resins in blends with polyamides give improved moisture resistance (473, 474). Other ingredients such as nitrogen compounds give modified polyamides which have greater film strength and durability (475).

The most important coating application for the neutral polyamide resins is in producing thixotropic coatings. Typical coating resins such as alkyds, modified alkyds, natural and synthetic ester oils, varnishes, and natural vegetable oils can be made thixotropic by the addition of dimer acids-based polyamide resins (476, 477, 478, 479, 480, 481, 482). Although usually only one polyamide is necessary, in some cases two different polyamide resins are used (483). Thixotrophy allows coatings to be produced which are gel-like, but which flow readily under application of a force such as a brush stroke. Thus, dripless paints are produced which are more convenient to apply (482).

In addition to the major application as hot-melt adhesives, in which no solvent is used, water-dispersible polyamide resins have been developed. These dispersions, called suspensoids, are useful in preparing water-based glues for household use. They are also useful in industrial applications in which hot-melt adhesives are inconvenient and solvents are undesirable.

Polyamide resin suspensoids having either excess amino groups or excess carboxylic acid groups have been prepared (484, 485, 486, 487, 488, 489). These can be made water-dispersible by reaction either of the free amino groups with water-soluble carboxylic acids, or by reaction of the free carboxylic acid groups with alkali.

Polyamide suspensoids are also useful as beater additives in paper production (490). These resins give paper wet-strength, bonding, and waterproof properties. Aminoamides and aminoimidazolines based on dimer acids are also useful for this purpose (491).

Treatment of cellulose fibers with mixtures of polyamides and isocyanates produce sheeting having excellent dry strength and flexibility properties (492). Non-woven fabrics are produced using polyamides as the binding agent (493, 494). Mixtures of polyamides and nitrocellulose are useful sizing agents for glass fibers (495). Polyamide resins containing excess amino groups can also be used to produce anti-static agents for textiles (496).

Dimer acids-based polyamides have been suggested for use in greases (497), as thickening agents for gasoline and other hydrocarbons for use in flame throwers, incendiary bombs and greases, and for transfer of fluid materials (498). They can be formulated to produce ashless detergent-dispersants for lubricating oils (499). Polyamides have been suggested for use as well-fracturing materials in crude-oil drilling (500). Polyamide resins are useful in forming fast-breaking emulsions (501, 502). They also impart water repellency and durability to hardened asphalt paving.

Miscellaneous applications include the use of neutral polyamides in solid-waste flocculation (503), as pigment dispersants (504), in cosmetics as bases for clear lipsticks (505), in making transparent candles (506, 507, 508), in decorative transfer decals (509, 510), and in detergents (511). There is intense activity in this product area; patents claiming new applications for polyamides based on dimer acids issue almost weekly.

b. *Applications of Reactive Polyamide Resins*

Reactive polyamide resins are produced by reacting dimer acids with aliphatic polyamines such as diethylenetriamine, triethylenetetramine, tetraethylenepentamine, and pentaethylenehexamine (512, 513, 514, 515, 516, 517, 518). The polyamine is considered to have the equivalent weight of a diamine, so that predominantly thermoplastic polymers containing unreacted primary and secondary amino groups are formed. These unreacted amino groups are, of course, capable of undergoing further reaction.

Among the many types of curing agents available to react with epoxy resins, the dimer acids-based reactive polyamides are especially useful. Epoxy resins cured with dimer acids-based polyamide resins have excellent flexibility, toughness, adhesion, chemical resistance, moisture resistance, and surface gloss. Curing may be effected either by melting the two resins together, or by mixing solvent solutions of the two resins. Curing occurs spontaneously and very rapidly in the absence of solvents, whereas it occurs more slowly when solvent solutions are used. Thus, polyamide-epoxy resin systems are suited for both surface coating and molding applications.

Major applications for the reactive polyamides include curing of epoxy compounds to form thermosetting surface coatings, adhesives, structural adhesives, casting and potting compounds, laminates, and various types of aggregate binding such as cement and asphalt. In addition, reactive polyamides are also used to a much smaller extent to cure phenolic resins, mainly for use in surface coatings and adhesives (519).

I. Surface Coatings

Surface coatings based on polyamide-epoxy resins have a satisfactory viscosity for brushing or spraying and may be applied in the absence of solvent (520). These films are flexible, resistant to chemicals and salt spray, do not yellow, and have good hardness and gloss. Varnishes with excellent flexibility and resistance to boiling water and alkali may be prepared by reacting polyamides with polyepoxide polyesters (521). The polyamide-epoxy coatings may be formulated to contain pigments or other fillers and they may be applied either in solvent solutions or by mixing just prior to use in the absence of solvents (522, 523, 524, 525).

Polyamide-epoxy resins with slower curing rates can be prepared using volatile carboxylic acids such as formic acid. The formic acid forms salts with amines and, as the formic acid evaporates, the amine is freed for reaction with the epoxy resin (526). Resins with very rapid drying rates can also be prepared. For example, polyamide resins blended with a Mannich base which contains both a tertiary amino group and a phenolic hydroxyl group react with epoxy resins to give coatings which are dust-free within thirty minutes (527).

Coatings suitable for electrical insulation applications can be prepared by reacting ether amine/polyamides with epoxides (528). These mixtures harden at room temperature to give tough, flexible, adherent coatings. A series of thermosetting epoxypolyamide powders, suitable for powder coating, can be prepared by reacting fatty guanamines based on dimer acids with epoxy resins (529).

Reactive polyamides can also be reacted with phenol-formaldehyde condensates (530), cresylic acid-formaldehyde resins (531), melamines (532), urea-formaldehyde resins, triazines (533), and isocyanates (534, 535). In all of these examples, the coatings have excellent properties of flexibility, hardness, and chemical resistance.

Since the polyamide-epoxy resins cure without the need for water or other curing agents, a wide variety of coating applications is possible, including simple surface coatings and coil coatings. An interesting application is the use of these resins to coat water-wet surfaces such as underwater supports and drilling rigs (536). Other uses include coatings for marking concrete and asphalt roads (537), marine finishes and swimming pool paints. They are also useful as primer coatings (538).

II. *Adhesives*

Reactive polyamides based on dimer acids can be reacted with epoxy resins or other polymers, such as phenolic resins, to produce thermosetting adhesives. These adhesives are commonly referred to as two-component adhesives, since the polyamide resin and the epoxy resin are packaged separately. They are mixed just prior to use. Upon application, curing begins in a short time to produce a strong, adherent bond. Epoxy-polyamide systems are especially useful because water is not a by-product of the curing reaction.

Compositions suitable for use as side-seam cements for metallic containers, plastic solders, auto body solders, caulking compounds, and in other adhesive applications are prepared by reacting polyamide resins containing available amino groups with epoxide resins (539, 540). Similarly, adhesives suitable for a variety of metal-to-metal bonding applications can be prepared (541). A mixture of the polyamide and epoxy can be formed into coils, rods, sheets, and webs, which can be stored at low temperatures ($-15°C$) without curing, but which react at room temperature (542). The resins can also be impregnated on tapes, which then can be applied separately to the surfaces to be adhered. Upon pressing, the two resins come in contact, causing adhesion (543). Self-locking bolts can be made by applying the polyamide and the epoxy resin to separate thread sections. When the bolt is tightened, the two resins mix and an adhesive bond is formed (544).

Although epoxy-polyamide resin systems form thermosetting adhesives, it is possible to blend them with other chemicals which cause them to act as thermoplastic adhesives. For example, blends of epoxy and polyamide resins with a thermoplastic carrier can be applied by melting but, once heated and applied, the adhesive becomes thermosetting (545). Certain types of plasticizers can also be used (546).

In addition to simple polyamide-epoxy resins, other resins may also be used. Phenolic resins (547), polysulfide resins (548), formaldehyde-amine condensates (549), and other resins capable of reacting with either polyamides or epoxies can be used. Similarly, various types of fillers such as cork, clays, and talc can be incorporated (550).

The polyamide-epoxy adhesive systems are similar to the polyamide-epoxy surface coatings and many of the references given in that section of this monograph also apply to adhesive applications. Generally, the polyamide-epoxy thermosetting adhesives are useful for bonding metals, plastics, wood, and films, where a strong adhesive is required. The polyamide-epoxy adhesives have excellent properties such as adhesion, flexibility, moisture and chemical resistance, and bonding strength.

III. *Other Applications*

Reactive polyamide resin-epoxy resin systems are used in potting and casting systems, e.g., to encapsulate electronic parts. The resins cure at room temperature, they do not shrink during curing, and the resulting product is flexible, impact resistant, durable, and resistant to attack by chemicals and moisture (528).

When applied to materials such as cellulosics, wool, and leather, polyamide-epoxy resins impart desirable properties. Cellulosic materials can be made waterproof, for example, and can be converted into materials suitable for use as containers, boxes, pipes, and even structural parts (551). Building compositions can also be prepared by curing epoxy-polyamide resins with various reinforcing agents such as cork and clay (552).

By treating cellulose or wool fibers with polyamide-epoxy

resins, these fibers can be made shrinkproof (553, 554, 555) and they can also be given a degree of permanent shape (556). Leather articles can be treated with the resins to improve scuff resistance and to give products having resistance to weathering (557, 558, 559). Non-woven fabrics can be produced by coating various types of fibers with epoxy-polyamide blends, which, upon compacting and heating, can be formed into sheets and shaped articles (560). In filament winding for reinforcing of various structures such as storage tanks, fiber glass treated with epoxy-polyamide resins is suitable for use (272).

Resins which give wet-strength to paper can be prepared by reacting reactive polyamides with epichlorohydrin (561, 562, 563). In these examples, the epoxy group becomes attached to the polyamide resin and reaction then occurs between the epoxy group and the hydroxyl groups of the cellulose.

Polyamide-epoxy resins are useful as binders in various types of building applications, including cements and mortars (564), grouting for tile (565), and trowel coatings (566). They may also be used as binders for patching and resurfacing concrete surfaces (567). Of special interest is the use of epoxy-polyamide resins as binders for asphalt, for use in building roads, walkways, and airport runways (568, 569). While relatively expensive, these roadbuilding materials are durable, resistant to stress-cracking, and resistant to many chemicals, oils, moisture, and salt compositions.

G. APPLICATIONS OF OTHER POLYMERIC NITROGEN DERIVATIVES OF DIMER ACIDS

Dimer dinitrile can be converted to polymeric secondary amines by hydrogenation at high pressure and temperature (200-290°C at 50 to 70 atm). They are useful as corrosion inhibitors, asphalt antistripping agents, flocculants, and antistatic agents (570). Such polyamines are claimed to be accelerators for rubber vulcanization. They improve the abrasion resistance of the cured stock and the tackiness of the uncured stock (571). An organic solvent solution of the polysecondary amines can be used to remove organic anionic material from aqueous solutions on contact (572). Alkylation of the polysecondary amines leads to polytertiary amines. A typical method is methylation with formaldehyde or formic acid. The products can be used as corrosion inhibitors and fuel-oil stabilizers (573).

Polyquaternary salts can be prepared either by the quaternization of the polyamines, or by polmerization of a dimer ditertiary amine and a dihalide. Reaction of methyl chloride with the polysecondary amine gives quarternary salts which are useful as flocculants, fabric softeners, biostats, and antistatic agents. Dihalides tend to lead to cross-linked products (574). Tertiary diamides prepared from dimer acids and a dialkyl amine are reduced to the tetraalkyl diamines and then quarternized with a dihalide. An example is the condensation product from N,N,N',N'-tetramethyl dimer diamine and 1,4-dichloro-2-butene. The principal suggested application for such compounds is the flocculation of slime. Other uses are as bentonite gelling agents, antistats, complexing agents, and biocides (575).

REFERENCES FOR CHAPTER FOUR

1. J. P. McDermott, U.S. Patent 2,631,979 (1953).
2. P. S. Landis and E. B. Backensto, U.S. Patent 2,632,695 (1953).
3. M. E. Gililand, J. R. Zoller and L. R. Burns, U.S. Patent 3,227,533 (1966).
4. T. L. Cantrell and J. G. Peters, U.S. Patent 2,773,032 (1956).
5. A. A. O'Kelly and C. A. Weltman, U.S. Patent 2,861,874 (1958).
6. A. E. Brehm, U.S. Patent 2,948,598 (1960).
7. F. K. Kawahara, U.S. Patent 2,972,526 (1961).
8. L. R. Stark, U.S. Patent 3,071,549 (1963).
9. F. A. Stuart and W. Lowe, U.S. Patent 3,208,945 (1965).
10. H. M. Rue, U.S. Patent 3,775,340 (1973).
11. P. J. Raifsnider and R. S. Treseder, U.S. Patent 2,763,612 (1956).
12. O. L. Riggs, Jr., and D. A. Shock, U.S. Patent 2,822,330 (1958).
13. O. L. Riggs, Jr., U.S. Patent 3,017,354 (1962).
14. K. H. Nimerick, U.S. Patent 3,378,488 (1968).
15. J. R. Stanford, U.S. Patent 3,412,024 (1968).
16. J. P. G. Beiswanger and J. W. Burnard, U.S. Patent 2,883,277 (1959).
17. T. W. Langer and B. F. Mago, U.S. Patent 2,624,708 (1953).
18. L. A. Joo and R. C. Kimble, U.S. Patent 3,267,038 (1966).
19. J. A. de Ridder and J. J. Freer, U.S. Patent 3,535,167 (1970).
20. E. P. Cunningham and D. W. Dinsmore, U.S. Patent 2,794,782 (1957).
21. H. J. Andress, Jr., and P. Y. C. Gee, U.S. Patent 3,251,663 (1966).
22. H. D. Marvel, U.S. Patent 3,304,162 (1967).
23. G. W. Eckert, U.S. Patent 3,346,355 (1967).
24. W. W. Scheumann, U.S. Patent 2,776,194 (1957).
25. N. E. Lemmon, H. D. Cook, and W. W. Frank, U.S. Patent 2,833,713 (1958).
26. E. E. Richardson and R. W. Watson, U.S. Patent 2,833,714 (1958).
27. M. J. Furey, U.S. Patent 3,180,832 (1965); 3,273,981 (1966).
28. R. B. Tierney and R. H. Krug, U.S. Patent 3,074,886 (1963).
29. R. B. Tierney and R. H. Krug, U.S. Patent 3,048,542 (1962).
30. C. Liddy, U.S. Patent 3,794,585 (1974).
31. A. C. Borg, U.S. Patent 3,113,107 (1963).
32. N. E. Lemmon and R. E. Karll, U.S. Patent 2,632,712 (1953).
33. P. M. Dwyer and G. A. Jedenoff, U.S. Patent 3,223,635 (1965).

34. V. A. Miller, U.S. Patent 3,640,860 (1972).
35. W. H. Shields and H. T. Buckley, U.S. Patent 2,944,920 (1960).
36. S. W. Tinsley, P. S. Starcher, C. W. McGary, Jr. and C. T. Patrick, Jr., U.S. Patent 3,019,202 (1962).
37. British Patent 1,001,467 (1965).
38. P. Mislow, *Official Digest Federation Paint and Varnish Clubs*, **30**, 277 (1958).
39. G. A. Salensky, U.S. Patent 3,449,274 (1969).
40. R. Chang and H. B. Arnold, U.S. Patent 3,371,070 (1968).
41. W. Guenther, H. Mosthaft and K. Bronstert, German Patent 1,174,069 (1964).
42. W. Guenther, E. Raber and H. Wild, German Patent 1,252,899 (1967).
43. L. W. Crovatt, Jr., U.S. Patent 3,329,633 (1967).
44. British Patent 904,798 (1962).
45. British Patent 1,082,239 (1967).
46. J. P. Bain, U.S. Patent 3,219,517 (1965).
47. R. H. Manley and C. D. Evans, U.S. Patent 2,357,839 (1944).
48. J. F. Abere, U.S. Patent 3,266,921 (1966).
49. D. A. Feigley, Jr. and L. N. Ray, Jr., U.S. Patent 3,093,609 (1963).
50. D. L. Kenaga, U.S. Patent 3,362,850 (1968).
51. W. P. Ericks, U.S. Patent 2,629,648 (1953).
52. J. F. Nobis and R. E. Robinson, U.S. Patent 2,914,578 (1959).
53. A. L. Ayers and C. R. Scott, U.S. Patent 2,643,260 (1953); 2,607,695 (1952).
54. J. C. Hillyer, U.S. Patent 2,490,437 (1949).
55. J. L. Lach, U.S. Patent 3,244,596 (1966).
56. J. D. Neesley, U.S. Patent 2,913,349 (1959).
57. F. H. Langenfeld and W. W. Overall, U.S. Patent 3,740,336 (1973).
58. G. W. Eckert and W. A. McDonald, U.S. Patent 3,549,313 (1970).
59. K. T. Mecklenborg, Private Communication (1973).
60. R. M. Peters, U. S. Patent 2,812,342 (1957).
61. G. J. Benoit, Jr., U.S. Patent 3,110,673 (1963).
62. R. T. Schlobohm and H. D. Millay, U.S. Patent 3,772,359 (1973).
63. D. H. Foelsch, U.S. Patent 3,527,705 (1970).
64. E. G. Lindstrom and M. R. Barusch, U.S. Patent 3,468,639 (1969).
65. R. T. Trites, U.S. Patent 3,493,512 (1970).
66. R. D. Aylesworth, B. R. Krabacher, R. G. Kadesch and N. O. V. Sonntag, U. S. Patent 3,074,981 (1963).
67. R. H. Boehringer and R. E. Vail, U.S. Patent 3,585,138 (1971).

68. R. W. Van Tuyle, U.S. Patent 3,071,546 (1963).
69. M. C. Weast, U.S. Patent 3,625,905 (1971).
70. L. F. Elmquist, U.S. Patent 3,442,695 (1969).
71. L. F. Elmquist, U.S. Patent 3,377,382 (1968).
72. R. W. Fisher and K. E. McCaleb, U.S. Patent 3,395,100 (1968).
73. K. H. Roberts and M. A. Gomolka, U.S. Patent 3,590,122 (1971).
74. R. R. Egan and B. J. Hoffman, Jr., *J. Amer. Oil Chem. Soc.*, **45**, 726 (1968).
75. G. Proserpio, *Cosmetics and Perfumery*, **89**, 45 (1974).
76. B. W. Landfried, H. J. Bassett and J. R. Moneymaker, U.S. Patent 3,515,562 (1970).
77. C. Zviak and J. Daeninckx, U.S. Patent 3,806,561 (1974).
78. T. J. Kondis and R. Rolles, U.S. Patent 3,781,177 (1973).
79. H.-J. Hartmann, G. Schnell, G. Werst, H. Grosselfinger, J.-W. Hartmann and H. Bipp, U.S. Patent 3,704,152 (1972).
80. W. E. Howard, German Patent 1,912,580 (1969).
81. T. Fukumaru, N. Hamma, H. Nakatani, H. Fukushima and K. Toki, U.S. Patent 3,784,577 (1947).
82. W. H. Machleder and R. R. Kuhn, U.S. Patent 3,782,912 (1974).
83. F. W. Moore and H. E. Vermillion, U.S. Patent 3,574,574 (1971).
84. G. W. Eckert, U.S. Patent 3,561,936 (1971).
85. G. W. Eckert, U.S. Patent 3,476,533 (1969).
86. J. G. Dadura, J. W. Wisner, Jr. and M. A. Wiley, U.S. Patent 3,321,402 (1967).
87. W. H. Kirkpatrick, V. L. Seale, A. Walker and J. B. Love, U.S. Patent 2,987,490 (1961).
88. C. E. Johnson, U. S. Patent 3,450,627 (1969).
89. E. Wittner, U.S. Patent 3,287,296 (1966).
90. D. L. Klass, W. L. Sieker and R. W. Watson, U.S. Patent 3,000,916 (1961).
91. G. Pruckmayr, U.S. Patent 3,745,135 (1973).
92. D. A. Feigley, Jr. and L. N. Ray, Jr., U.S. Patent 2,940,892 (1960).
93. M. H. Keck, U.S. Patent 3,649,571 (1972).
94. A. Nishimura, U.S. Patent 3,580,874 (1971).
95. G. A. Lessells and L. J. Rekers, U.S. Patent 3,205,185 (1965).
96. B. Dobinson, P. Hope, K. Winterbottom and T. Shaw, German Patent 2,054,878 (1971).
97. A. J. Barber, D. J. R. Massy, J. McCartney and K. Winterbottom, German Patent 2,217,236 (1972).
98. R. E. Layman, Jr., U.S. Patent 3,719,620 (1973).
99. B. G. Barron, U.S. Patent 3,649,389 (1972).
100. H. E. Marsh, Jr. and J. J. Hutckinson, U.S. Patent 3,557,027 (1971).

101. H. F. Krackenberger and D. J. Smith, U.S. Patent 3,749,616 (1973).
102. F. O. Barrett and C. G. Goebel, German Patent 1,280,853 (1968).
103. Emery Industries, Inc., Technical Bulletin 438D.
104. W. C. Simpson, U.S. Patent 2,956,034 (1960).
105. British Patent 996,499 (1965).
106. British Patent 883,523 (1961).
107. British Patent 960,911 (1964).
108. W. Shoen, U.S. Patent 3,260,669 (1966).
109. W. H. Kirkpatrick and V. L. Seale, U.S. Patent 2,935,474 (1960).
110. E. E. Clayton, Jr., U.S. Patent 3,258,424 (1966).
111. P. W. Fischer, U.S. Patent 3,151,138 (1964).
112. H. G. Smith and T. L. Cantrell, U.S. Patent 2,830,021 (1958).
113. A. E. Brehm and A. W. Lindert, U.S. Patent 2,880,095 (1959).
114. A. Sterlin, U.S. Patent 2,773,879 (1956).
115. A. Sterlin, U.S. Patent 2,945,821 (1960).
116. A. Sterlin, U.S. Patent 2,994,596 (1961).
117. D. B. Sheldahl and T. O. Counts, U.S. Patent 3,017,257 (1962).
118. A. R. Sabol, E. W. Blaha and R. E. Koskie, U.S. Patent 3,109,814 (1963).
119. R. H. Hausler and L. A. Goeller, U.S. Patent 3,696,048 (1972).
120. R. H. Hausler and L. A. Goeller, U.S. Patent 3,696,049 (1972).
121. J. I. Wasson and A. J. Morway, U.S. Patent 2,737,497 (1956).
122. C. B. Biswell, U.S. Patent 2,584,784 (1952).
123. J. J. Plemich, U.S. Patent 3,006,849 (1961).
124. C. E. Santangelo and B. H. Krees, U.S. Patent 2,992,145 (1961).
125. H. A. Cyba, U.S. Patent 3,017,360 (1962).
126. H. D. C. Hill, U.S. Patent 3,336,123 (1967).
127. K. D. Ashley and S. Mason, U.S. Patent 2,555,104 (1951).
128. W. A. Young and J. C. Zaborski, U.S. Patent 2,626,897 (1953).
129. W. K. Dean, U.S. Patent 2,620,345 (1952).
130. British Patent 708,985 (1954).
131. R. D. Aylesworth and L. A. Stegemeyer, U.S. Patent 2,795,492 (1957).
132. J. H. Lux and K. Parker, U.S. Patent 2,699,428 (1955).
133. J. R. Allison, U.S. Patent 2,899,389 (1959).
134. G. W. Eckert and P. R. Thomas, U.S. Patent 2,983,680 (1961).
135. A. J. Morway and A. J. Bodner, U.S. Patent 3,314,886 (1967).

136. M. A. Whitfield and J. B. Dobbs, U.S. Patent 3,285,718 (1966).
137. R. E. Layman, Jr., U.S. Patent 3,025,251 (1962).
138. W. L. Hensley, U.S. Patent 3,065,109 (1962).
139. C. Penoyer, U.S. Patent 2,978,346 (1961).
140. Belgian Patent 672,321 (1966).
141. W. Offermann and H. Linden, U.S. Patent 3,386,845 (1968).
142. E. M. Geiser, U.S. Patent 3,037,875 (1962).
143. Belgian Patent 658,915 (1965).
144. British Patent 1,081,940 (1967).
145. D. A. Feigley, Jr. and L. N. Ray, Jr., U.S. Patent 3,008,868 (1961).
146. British Patent 891,745 (1960).
147. British Patent 958,081 (1964).
148. G. B. Young, U.S. Patent 3,014,783 (1961).
149. A. M. Snow, Jr., U.S. Patent 3,651,037 (1972).
150. A. M. Snow, Jr., U.S. Patent 3,651,038 (1972).
151. R. Kelly and E. J. Ritter, U.S. Patent 3,538,009 (1970).
152. R. Kelly and E. J. Ritter, U.S. Patent 3,630,934 (1971).
153. R. Kelly and E. J. Ritter, U.S. Patent 3,798,182 (1974); 3,813,350 (1974).
154. R. B. Tierney, U.S. Patent 2,922,763 (1960).
155. R. B. Tierney, R. H. Krug and R. P. Chesluk, U.S. Patent 2,930,758 (1960).
156. British Patent 847,399 (1960).
157. C. J. Henry and R. B. Tierney, U.S. Patent 3,039,967 (1962).
158. M. J. Furey, J. K. Appeldoorn and A. F. Turbak, U.S. Patent 3,287,273 (1966).
159. A. H. Matuszak and W. J. Craven, U.S. Patent 2,849,399 (1958).
160. T. W. Mastin, German Patent 1,932,212 (1970).
161. V. L. Larimer, U.S. Patent 3,391,161 (1968).
162. J. I. Wasson and J. C. Zimmer, U.S. Patent 2,417,281 (1947).
163. M. Rosenberg, U.S. Patent 3,492,232 (1970).
164. R. J. Sturwold and F. O. Barrett, U.S. Patent 3,769,215 (1973).
165. R. I. Gottshall and H. W. Swain, U.S. Patent 3,017,359 (1962).
166. A. J. Morway, D. W. Young and D. L. Cottle, U.S. Patent 2,673,184 (1954).
167. G. E. Barker, U.S. Patent 2,758,976 (1956); 2,841,560 (1958).
168. G. E. Barker, U.S. Patent 2,755,251 (1956); 2,767,145 (1956).
169. British Patent 764,922 (1957).
170. W. E. Parker, H. B. Knight, R. E. Koos and W. C. Ault, U.S. Patent 3,393,214 (1968).
171. British Patent 621,104 (1949).
172. R. H. Keinle and G. P. Whitcomb, U.S. Patent 2,473,798 (1949); 2,606,199 (1952); Canadian Patent 498,969 (1954).

173. M. De Groote, U.S. Patent 3,057,890 (1962); 3,057,892 (1962).
174. M. De Groote, U.S. Patent 2,417,738 (1947).
175. L. A. Fluck and A. L. Logan, U.S. Patent 2,718,478 (1955).
176. E. S. Lutton, U.S. Patent 3,353,967 (1967).
177. E. S. Lutton and N. B. Tucker, U.S. Patent 3,367,782 (1968).
178. D. D. Staker, R. H. Plantholt and D. J. Kriege, U.S. Patent 3,649,657 (1972); 3,776,928 (1973).
179. R. I. Gottshall and R. T. Kern, Jr., U.S. Patent 2,902,499 (1959); 2,975,133 (1961).
180. W. B. Hughes and V. L. Stromberg, U.S. Patent 2,987,521 (1961).
181. J. P. Copes, U.S. Patent 2,976,245 (1961).
182. P. W. Fischer, U.S. Patent 2,805,201 (1957).
183. R. T. Kern, Jr., and J. G. Peters, U.S. Patent 2,789,951 (1957).
184. E. L. Humphreys and W. B. Morse, U.S. Patent 3,785,975 (1974).
185. British Patent 1,048,996 (1966).
186. C. A. Cohen, U.S. Patent 3,326,826 (1967).
187. S. Penczek, *Battelle Tech. Review*, **7**, 773a (1958).
188. S. B. Crecelius, U.S. Patent 2,698,308 (1954).
189. M. H. Keck and J. R. Wilson, U.S. Patent 3,390,108 (1968).
190. Belgian Patent 649,158 (1964).
191. R. W. Van Tuyle, U.S. Patent 3,470,212 (1969); 3,544,503 (1970).
192. J. Dazzi, U.S. Patent 2,630,441 (1953).
193. R. Ernst, U.S. Patent 3,167,554 (1965).
194. W. B. Hughes, U.S. Patent 2,646,399 (1953).
195. D. L. Klass, W. L. Sieker and R. W. Watson, U.S. Patent 3,000,916 (1961); 3,113,106 (1963).
196. A. G. Rocchini, U.S. Patent 2,718,503 (1955).
197. H. A. Cyba, U.S. Patent 3,074,990 (1963).
198. O. Turinsky, U.S. Patent 2,607,783 (1952).
199. J. A. Dixon, U.S. Patent 2,756,213 (1956).
200. D. B. Eickemeyer, T. S. Chao and M. Kjonaas, U.S. Patent 3,256,196 (1966).
201. M. J. Furey and H. J. Schugar, U.S. Patent 3,321,404 (1967).
202. M. J. Furey, U.S. Patent 3,281,358 (1966).
203. E. L. Skau, R. R. Mod and F. C. Magne, U.S. Patent 3,219,612 (1965); 3,336,319 (1967).
204. F. C. Magne, E. L. Skau and R. R. Mod, U.S. Patent 3,260,692 (1966); 3,250,635 (1966).
205. F. C. Magne, R. R. Mod and E. L. Skau, *J. Amer. Oil Chem. Soc.*, **45**, 567 (1968).
206. J. Dazzi, U.S. Patent 2,965,591 (1960).
207. R. R. Mod, F. C. Magne and E. L. Skau, *J. Amer. Oil Chem. Soc.*, **41**, 781 (1964).

208. R. L. Wear, B. Oiye and A. S. Winthrop, U.S. Patent 2,970,972 (1961).
209. W. Neumann and E. Zankl, U.S. Patent 3,183,109 (1965).
210. G. F. Scherer, U.S. Patent 3,256,182 (1966).
211. J. O. Hendricks and A. F. Schmelzle, U.S. Patent 2,653,880 (1953).
212. L. E. Gast, W. Schneider and J. C. Cowan, *J. Amer. Oil Chem. Soc.*, **43**, 418 (1966).
213. Netherlands Patent 6,502,063 (1966).
214. British Patent 1,032,873 (1966).
215. M. R. Kamal, U. S. Patent 3,267,080 (1966).
216. C. Burba, M. Drawert and E. Griebsch, U.S. Patent 3,578,612 (1971).
217. J. T. Thurston and R. B. Warner, U.S. Patent 2,470,081 (1949).
218. H. E. Millson and S. Mooradian, Canadian Patent 503,030 (1954).
219. J. T. Thurston and R. B. Warner, U.S. Patent 2,537,493 (1951).
220. D. W. Young and D. L. Cottle, U.S. Patent 2,683,132 (1954).
221. J. Nixon and F. L. Jonach, U.S. Patent 3,637,357 (1972).
222. A. W. Schwab, J. A. Stolp, L. E. Gast and J. C. Cowan, *J. Amer. Oil Chem. Soc.*, **43**, 30 (1966).
223. W. B. Johnston, U.S. Patent 2,347,562 (1944).
224. British Patent 1,132,033 (1968).
225. J. R. Caldwell and R. Gilkey, U.S. Patent 3,091,600 (1963).
226. British Patent 994,441 (1965).
227. British Patent 1,065,734 (1967).
228. W. Seeliger, U.S. Patent 3,359,242 (1967).
229. British Patent 1,025,547 (1966).
230. British Patent 1,023,140 (1966).
231. H.-J. Krause and M. Dohr, Canadian Patent 725,692 (1966).
232. British Patent 1,194,583 (1970).
233. W. Offermann, A. Kirstahler and W. Stein, German Patent 1,253,848 (1967).
234. G. Walther and W. Stein, U.S. Patent 3,281,374 (1966).
235. Belgian Patent 701,370 (1968).
236. Belgian Patent 669,009 (1966).
237. For an analogous example, see: M. J. Astle, *Industrial Organic Nitrogen Compounds,* ACS Monograph Series No. 150, Reinhold Publishing Corporation, 1961, New York, N.Y., p. 24.
238. L. R. Vertnik and H. Wittcoff, U.S. Patent 3,242,141 (1966).
239. L. R. Vertnik and H. Wittcoff, U.S. Patent 3,231,545 (1966).
240. E. R. Rogier, U.S. Patent 3,239,546 (1966).
241. M. R. Kamal, U.S. Patent 3,284,416 (1966).
242. D. E. Peerman and L. R. Vertnik, U.S. Patent 3,483,237 (1969).

243. D. Magay, U.S. Patent 3,803,103 (1974).
244. M. R. Kamal and D. E. Floyd, U.S. Patent 3,481,774 (1969).
245. R. C. Kuder, U.S. Patent 3,639,338 (1972).
246. B. R. Appel, U.S. Patent 3,438,929 (1969).
247. L. R. Vertnik and H. Wittcoff, U.S. Patent 3,475,406 (1969).
248. M. R. Kamal, U.S. Patent 3,726,921 (1973).
249. M. R. Kamal and J. L. Keen, U.S. Patent 3,589,978 (1971).
250. A. G. Janssen, U.S. Patent 3,539,386 (1970).
251. H. A. Wittcoff and K. B. Stokes, U.S. Patent 3,589,932 (1971).
252. C. W. Jonaitis and L. E. Elmquist, U.S. Patent 3,629,319 (1971).
253. J. M. Butler, U. S. Patent 3,459,712 (1969).
254. French Patent 1,545,442 (1968).
255. W. M. Sims, U.S. Patent 3,692,730 (1972).
256. W. M. Sims, U.S. Patent 3,668,171 (1972).
257. J. L. Keen, U.S. Patent 3,619,357 (1971).
258. D. L. Andersen, U.S. Patent 2,913,305 (1959).
259. R. Fisher, L. R. Vertnik, K. E. McCaleb and N. M. LeBard, U.S. Patent 3,201,471 (1965).
260. K. E. McCaleb, L. R. Vertnik and D. L. Andersen, U.S. Patent 3,010,782 (1961).
261. British Patent 835,678 (1960).
262. R. L. Wakeman and J. F. Coates, U.S. Patent 3,328,409 (1967).
263. A. B. Sveum and J. F. Zalar, U.S. Patent 3,299,138 (1967).
264. J. Maddox, Jr. and W. Schoen, U.S. Patent 3,623,979 (1971); 3,687,847 (1972).
265. W. B. Hughes, U.S. Patent 2,940,927 (1960).
266. W. B. Hughes and V. L. Stromberg, U.S. Patent 3,017,352 (1962).
267. W. B. Hughes and V. L. Stromberg, U.S. Patent 3,018,246 (1962).
268. A. H. Smith, U.S. Patent 2,967,868 (1961).
269. V. L. Stromberg and A. H. Smith, U.S. Patent 2,917,376 (1959).
270. J. A. Williams and A. G. Hirsch, U.S. Patent 3,020,199 (1962).
271. W. B. Hughes, Canadian Patent 550,268 (1957).
272. L. R. Vertnik, U.S. Patent 3,271,350 (1966).
273. H. B. Arnold, U.S. Patent 3,267,172 (1966); 3,344,089 (1967).
274. D. E. Peerman, U.S. Patent 3,214,403 (1965).
275. D. E. Peerman, U.S. Patent 3,214,324 (1965).
276. British Patent 965,588 (1964).
277. D. E. Peerman, U.S. Patent 3,214,409 (1965).
278. J. T. Thurston, U.S. Patent 2,483,986 (1949).
279. J. C. Cowan and W. C. Ault, U.S. Patent 2,373,015 (1945).
280. J. C. Cowan and H. M. Teeter, U.S. Patent 2,384,443 (1945).

281. J. C. Cowan and D. H. Wheeler, U.S. Patent 2,429,219 (1947).
282. E. W. Eckey and J. E. Taylor, U.S. Patent 2,413,613 (1946).
283. T. Laakso, U.S. Patent 3,311,578 (1967).
284. A. A. Mohajer and P. R. Thomas, U.S. Patent 3,383,343 (1968).
285. German Patent 2,032,818 (1971).
286. French Patent 1,398,551 (1965).
287. French Patent 1,398,552 (1965).
288. British Patent 1,035,999 (1966).
289. British Patent 1,142,770 (1969).
290. P. Penczek, Z. Klosowski and R. Ostrysz, *Plaste Kautschuk,* **10** (5), 262 (1963); *Chem. Abs.* **60,** 3173e (1964).
291. E. E. Parker, U.S. Patent 3,448,066 (1969).
292. C. A. Siconolfi and B. L. Swanson, U.S. Patent 3,488,305 (1970).
293. German Patent 1,815,526 (1969).
294. French Patent 1,550,254 (1968).
295. Belgian Patent 714,797 (1968).
296. H. Dannenberg and T. F. Bradley, U.S. Patent 2,564,395 (1951).
297. E. L. Clark, U.S. Patent 3,367,895 (1968).
298. W. J. Sparks and D. W. Young, U.S. Patent 2,625,526 (1953).
299. A. M. Partansky, U.S. Patent 2,967,838 (1961).
300. B. deSurville, *J. recherches centre natl. recherche sci., Lab. Belle-vue* (Paris), **No. 30,** 169 (1955); *Chem. Abs.,* **49,** 16466d (1955).
301. German Patent 2,159,669 (1972).
302. A. J. Soliday, U.S. Patent 3,763,064 (1973).
303. M. T. O'Gorman and J. D. Downs, U.S. Patent 3,530,082 (1970).
304. South African Patent 67 06,177 (1968); *Chem. Abs.,* **70,** 48692z (1969).
305. F. Fekete and J. S. McNally, U.S. Patent 3,674,727 (1972).
306. A. J. Coury, U.S. Patent 3,549,570 (1970).
307. L. H. Dunlap and J. A. Parker, U.S. Patent 2,873,201 (1959).
308. C. M. Carson, U.S. Patent 2,496,934 (1950).
309. D. A. Rogers, Jr., and R. J. Hillen, U.S. Patent 3,026,222 (1962).
310. British Patent 998,654 (1965).
311. D. D. Taft and T. H. Shepler, U.S. Patent 3,758,431 (1973).
312. W. J. Jackson, Jr. and W. R. Darnell, U.S. Patent 3,795,644 (1974).
313. E. W. Wilson and J. E. Hutchins, U.S. Patent 3,194,791 (1965).
314. D. W. Young and W. J. Sparks, U.S. Patent 2,491,350 (1949).
315. J. A. Verdol, U.S. Patent 3,170,898 (1965); 2,944,025 (1960).
316. Belgian Patent 680,840 (1966).
317. British Patent 1,053,183 (1966).

318. British Patent 1,057,233 (1967).
319. M. J. Furey, Canadian Patent 753,622 (1967).
320. C. Lion, U.S. Patent 3,390,083 (1968).
321. W. J. Sparks and D. W. Young, U.S. Patent 2,424,588 (1947).
322. R. H. Boehringer, R. D. Aylesworth and W. E. Utz, U.S. Patent 3,472,775 (1969).
323. D. W. Young and W. J. Sparks, U.S. Patent 2,435,619 (1948).
324. D. W. Young and J. P. Rocca, U.S. Patent 2,497,968 (1950).
325. E. W. Cook and T. F. Bradley, U.S. Patent 2,325,040 (1943).
326. R. I. Gottshall and R. T. Kern, U.S. Patent, 2,767,144 (1956).
327. W. B. Hughes and V. L. Stromberg, U.S. Patent 3,014,864 (1961).
328. K. H. Nimerick, U.S. Patent 3,692,675 (1972).
329. F. A. Stuart, W. T. Stewart, W. Lowe and F. W. Kavanagh, U.S. Patent 3,083,187 (1963).
330. C. F. Brown, U.S. Patent 2,450,578 (1948).
331. C. M. Blair, Jr., U.S. Patent 2,562,878 (1951).
332. W. H. Kirkpatrick, U.S. Patent 2,950,299 (1960).
333. A. Walker, V. L. Seale and W. H. Kirkpatrick, U.S. Patent 2,971,923 (1961).
334. M. De Groote, U.S. Patent 2,652,388 (1953).
335. W. H. Kirkpatrick and A. Walker, U.S. Patent 2,723,960 (1955).
336. L. A. Fluck and A. L. Logan, Canadian Patent 546,525 (1957).
337. T. P. Dumont, U.S. Patent 3,694,257 (1972).
338. British Patent 428,864 (1935).
339. F. H. Lyons, U.S. Patent 2,734,879 (1956).
340. W. P. Cody, U.S. Patent, 2,922,769 (1960).
341. J. A. Parker, U.S. Patent 2,669,338 (1961).
342. Belgian Patent 611,204 (1962).
343. R. E. Layman, U.S. Patent 3,158,584 (1964).
344. A. Salgado and A. R. Manyak, U.S. Patent 3,124,550 (1964); 3,124,549 (1964).
345. D. Laganis, U.S. Patent 3,479,307 (1969).
346. British Patent 1,257,697 (1971).
347. L. V. Hassel and J. A. Parker, U.S. Patent 2,773,782 (1956).
348. J. A. Parker and E. J. Pieper, U.S. Patent 2,813,841 (1957).
349. D. D. Ritson and R. E. Layman, Jr., U.S. Patent 3,384,509 (1968).
350. M. M. Donaldson and D. R. Sexsmith, U.S. Patent 3,377,187 (1968).
351. S. O. Greenlee and J. D. Zech, U.S. Patent 2,502,518 (1950).
352. J. B. Boylan, *Paint Varn. Prod.*, **56** (11), 71 (1966); *Chem. Abs.*, **66,** 11905n (1967).
353. J. D. Garber, D. Wasserman and R. A. Gasser, U.S. Patent 3,358,005 (1967).
354. D. Laganis, U.S. Patent 3,498,940 (1970).

355. German Patent 1,925,349 (1970).
356. Belgian Patent 569,062 (1958).
357. J. J. Seiwert and J. B. Boylan, U.S. Patent 3,406,134 (1968).
358. A. Santaniello, U.S. Patent 3,264,236 (1966).
359. R. D. Aylesworth, R. H. Boehringer, D. T. Moore and M. H. Smith, *Modern Plastics,* **35** (9), 145 (1958); *Chem. Abs.,* **52,** 9649d (1958).
360. R. J. Ferrari, J. W. Sinner, J. C. Bill and W. F. Brucksch, *Ind. Eng. Chem.,* **50** (7), 1041 (1958).
361. E. Simon and F. W. Thomas, U.S. Patent 2,802,795 (1957).
362. British Patent 809,697 (1959).
363. British Patent 837,997 (1960).
364. L. R. LeBras and R. E. Park, U.S. Patent 3,068,254 (1962).
365. T. E. Yeates and C. M. Thierfelder, U.S. Patent 3,173,887 (1965).
366. Belgian Patent 677,623 (1966).
367. British Patent 1,032,233 (1966).
368. Belgian Patent 686,985 (1967).
369. British Patent 1,086,795 (1967).
370. French Patent 2,013,912 (1970).
371. D. E. Terry and D. H. Wheeler, U.S. Patent 2,458,484 (1949).
372. J. E. Masters, Canadian Patent 569,227 (1959).
373. J. E. Masters, U.S. Patent 3,280,056 (1966).
374. British Patent 1,012,047 (1965).
375. C. V. Wittenwyler, *Chem. Eng. News,* **42,** 52 (March 16, 1964).
376. W. M. Boyer, G. Galvin and H. E. Tarbell, Jr., U.S. Patent 3,031,421 (1962).
377. W. C. Simpson, T. F. Mika and J. C. Illman, U.S. Patent 3,136,668 (1964).
378. Belgian Patent 607,395 (1962).
379. G. B. Payne and C. W. Smith, U.S. Patent 2,870,170 (1959).
380. German Patent 1,931,292 (1970).
381. German Patent 1,942,653 (1970).
382. Swiss Patent 520,726 (1972); *Chem. Abs.,* **77,** 62764a (1972).
383. German Patent 1,930,108 (1970).
384. German Patent 2,003,007 (1970).
385. R. Schmid, F. Lohse, W. Fisch and H. Batzer, U.S. Patent 3,557,035 (1971); 3,557,036 (1971); 3,642,674 (1972).
386. Belgian Patent 572,736 (1959).
387. H. A. Newey, U.S. Patent 2,940,986 (1960).
388. T. F. Bradley and H. J. Sommer, U.S. Patent 3,015,635 (1962).
389. British Patent 1,007,558 (1965).
390. D. Neal and J. A. Lopez, U.S. Patent 3,356,624 (1967).
391. J. A. Lopez and J. R. Hallstrom, U.S. Patent 3,446,762 (1969).
392. E. B. Tanner, U.S. Patent 3,355,401 (1967).
393. Belgian Patent 693,297 (1967).
394. British Patent 988,410 (1965).

395. Belgian Patent 646,631 (1964).
396. R. Scheibli, U.S. Patent 3,219,602 (1965).
397. R. Scheibli, U.S. Patent 3,219,603 (1965).
398. E. R. Rogier, U.S. Patent 3,228,911 (1966).
399. R. G. Swanson and A. N. Walus, U.S. Patent 3,272,647 (1966).
400. J. B. Boylan, *Treatise on Coatings,* Vol. 1, *Film Forming Compositions.* Part 3, R. R. Myers, and J. S. Long, Eds., Raymond R. Dekker, Inc., New York, N.Y., 1972, pp. 1-76; *Chem. Abs.,* **76,** 155631z (1972).
401. T. F. Bradley, U.S. Patent 2,379,413 (1945).
402. J. C. Cowan, L. B. Falkenburg, H. M. Teeter and P.S. Skell, U.S. Patent 2,450,940 (1948).
403. L. B. Falkenburg, H. M. Teeter, P. S. Skell and J. C. Cowan, *Oil and Soap,* **22,** 143, (1945).
404. *Chemical Economics Handbook,* Stanford Research Institute, Menlo Park, California, p. 581.1031D, 581.1031H, March, 1974.
405. D. J. Carlick and W. J. Russell, U.S. Patent 3,156,572 (1964).
406. D. E. Floyd and D. W. Glaser, U.S. Patent 3,037,871 (1962); Belgian Patent 586,415 (1960).
407. A. J. Dunne and K. A. Bownes, U.S. Patent 3,034,997 (1962).
408. S. Zweig, U.S. Patent 2,788,287 (1957).
409. British Patent 1,076,974 (1967).
410. British Patent 1,101,211 (1969).
411. K. Tashiro and Y. Matsunami, Japanese Patent 70 22,349 (1970).
412. H. Tashiro and A. Tanaka, Japanese Patent 69 32,066 (1969).
413. H. Tashiro, U.S. Patent 3,597,376 (1971).
414. South African Patent 67 05,038 (1968).
415. British Patent 1,246,347 (1971).
416. M. Drawert, E. Griebsch, B. Krieger, H. Schepp and C. Burba, German Patent 2,128,984 (1973); British Patent 1,129,595 (1968).
417. S. V. Hammond, German Patent 1,929,005 (1969).
418. A. H. Gruben and D. J. Carlick, U.S. Patent 3,639,313 (1972).
419. M. Drawert and W. Lippe, U.S. Patent 3,622,604 (1971).
420. D. E. Floyd and D. W. Glaser, U.S. Patent 3,224,893 (1965).
421. J. G. Antonak and W. Schweitzer, British Patent 1,067,776 (1967).
422. Belgian Patent 670,980 (1966).
423. D. W. Glaser and D. E. Floyd, U.S. Patent 3,253,940 (1966).
424. C. I. Atherton, British Patent 1,083,155 (1967).
425. D. E. Floyd and D. W. Glaser, U.S. Patent 3,412,115 (1968).
426. D. W. Glaser, U.S. Patent 3,522,270 (1970).
427. A. F. Wilson, U.S. Patent 3,420,789 (1969).
428. H. Tashiro and Y. Matsunami, Japanese Patent 72 26,197 (1972).

429. H. Tashiro and A. Tanaka, Japanese Patent 69 32,067 (1969).
430. H. J. Sharkey and R. J. Sturwold, U.S. Patent 3,700,618 (1972).
431. D. W. Glaser and R. A. Lovald, U.S. Patent 3,776,865 (1973); 3,778,394 (1973).
432. P. D. Whyzmuzis and C. W. Wilkus, U.S. Patent 3,786,007 (1974).
433. D. E. Peerman and H. Wittcoff, U.S. Patent 2,886,543 (1959).
434. J. H. Groves, U.S. Patent 2,840,264 (1958); Canadian Patent 571,184 (1959).
435. J. H. Groves and G. G. Wilson, U.S. Patent 2,839,219 (1958).
436. E. C. Johnson and R. D. Clarke, U.S. Patent 2,975,150 (1961).
437. R. E. Vetter, U.S. Patent 2,653,881 (1953).
438. S. M. Terry, U.S. Patent 2,635,974 (1953).
439. C. M. Keaton, U.S. Patent 2,495,008 (1950).
440. F. B. Speyer, Canadian Patent 563,610 (1958).
441. D. Aelony, U.S. Patent 2,955,951 (1960).
442. L. R. Vertnik, U.S. Patent 3,408,317 (1968).
443. D. E. Floyd, R. J. Ess and L. R. Vertnik, U.S. Patent 3,396,180 (1968).
444. F. O. Barrett, U.S. Patent 3,595,816 (1971).
445. Belgian Patent 713,050 (1968); 678,870 (1966).
446. Belgian Patent 694,680 (1967).
447. Belgian Patent 664,294 (1965).
448. Netherlands Appl. 6,612,615 (1967).
449. British Patent 1,136,250 (1968).
450. Belgian Patent 667,864 (1966).
451. E. Griebsch and M. Drawert, Belgian Patent 713,051 (1968); U.S. Patent 3,499,853 (1970).
452. British Patent 1,055,676 (1967).
453. S. V. Hammond, German Patent 2,146,162 (1972).
454. K. Uno, S. Nishimura, M. Nishimura and K. Amari, Japanese Patent 72 00,520 (1972).
455. M. Drawert and E. Griebsch, German Patent 1,908,754 (1970).
456. British Patent 1,129,595 (1968).
457. L. R. Vertnik, French Patent 1,581,969 (1969); U.S. Patent 3,664,980 (1972).
458. E. R. Rogier, U.S. Patent 3,717,598 (1973).
459. R. J. Sturwold and H. J. Sharkey, U.S. Patent 3,738,950 (1973).
460. H. Tashiro, Japanese Patent 70 09,390 (1970).
461. O. Kettenring and W. Gotze, U.S. Patent 3,449,273 (1969).
462. D. R. Pitz and A. W. Kehe, U.S. Patent 3,496,060 (1970).
463. L. B. Falkenburg, A. J. Lewis and J. C. Cowan, U.S. Patent 2,550,682 (1951).
464. German Patent 1,062,372 (1959).
465. Netherlands Patent 6,604,144 (1966).

466. W. B. Horback and G. M. Moelter, U.S. Patent 2,689,800 (1954).
467. A. O. Allen, T. M. Murray and F. P. Liberti, U.S. Patent 2,754,217 (1956).
468. E. T. Rayner, D. A. Yeadon, L. L. Hopper, Jr., H. P. Dupuy and F. G. Dollear, U.S. Patent 3,312,565 (1967).
469. H. Wittcoff and M. M. Renfrew, U.S. Patent 2,695,908 (1954).
470. L. J. Gold, U.S. Patent 2,451,212 (1948).
471. A. A. House, U.S. Patent 3,377,305 (1968).
472. A. E. Young and K. D. Bacon, U.S. Patent 2,517,754 (1950).
473. Belgian Patent 678,508 (1966).
474. K. W. Fries, U.S. Patent 2,469,108 (1949).
475. H. H. Young and S. B. Luce, U.S. Patent 2,992,195 (1961).
476. W. B. Winkler, U.S. Patent 2,663,649 (1953).
477. N. F. Toussaint and T. J. Anagnostou, U.S. Patent 2,962,461 (1960).
478. H. J. Wright, D. R. McGuire and P. F. Westfall, U.S. Patent 2,861,048 (1958).
479. W. Goetze and E. Griebsch, Canadian Patent 688,937 (1964); U.S. Patent 3,141,787 (1964).
480. Belgian Patent 573,375 (1958).
481. British Patent 996,511 (1965).
482. E. J. Aronoff, A. Weber, T. A. Augurt and J. A. Ciuffo, U.S. Patent 3,254,040 (1966).
483. A. R. H. Tawn and A. F. Wilson, U.S. Patent 3,178,302 (1965); British Patent 973,963 (1964).
484. H. Wittcoff, U.S. Patent 2,728,737 (1955); Canadian Patent 511,578 (1955).
485. D. Aelony, U.S. Patent 2,908,584 (1959).
486. H. Wittcoff, U.S. Patent 2,824,848 (1958).
487. H. Wittcoff and W. A. Jordan, U.S. Patent 2,811,459 (1957).
488. H. Wittcoff and M. M. Renfrew, U.S. Patent 2,768,090 (1956).
489. H. Wittcoff, U.S. Patent 2,926,117 (1960).
490. M. M. Renfrew, H. Wittcoff and N. A. Kjelson, U.S. Patent 2,767,089 (1956); Canadian Patent 563,952 (1958).
491. D. E. Floyd, R. J. Ess, J. L. Keen and J. W. Opie, U.S. Patent 3,138,473 (1964).
492. G. R. Nelson, U.S. Patent 3,233,962 (1966).
493. D. E. Peerman and H. van Demmeltraadt, U.S. Patent 3,717,528 (1973).
494. R. Grossteinbeck, G. Tepel and W. Schulze, Canadian Patent 756,970 (1967).
495. L. P. Biefeld and J. P. Stalego, U.S. Patent 2,671,744 (1954); C. A. Smucker and J. P. Stalego, U.S. Patent 3,322,702 (1967).

496. E. I. Valko, G. C. Tesoro and E. D. Szubin, U.S. Patent 2,882,185 (1959).
497. British Patent 774,084 (1957).
498. D. E. Floyd, U.S. Patent 2,662,068 (1953).
499. British Patent 973,679 (1964).
500. P. H. Cardwell, L. H. Eilers and A. Park, U.S. Patent 2,802,531 (1957).
501. H. V. Moore, G. D. Edwards and M. Lichtenwalter, U.S. Patent 3,046,149 (1962).
502. E. W. Mertens and J. R. Wright, U.S. Patent 3,026,266 (1962); J. R. Wright and E. W. Mertens, U.S. Patent 3,062,829 (1962).
503. British Patent 906,854 (1962).
504. R. Langley, N. Mearns and R. B. McKay, U.S. Patent 3,732,118 (1973).
505. S. J. Strianse and M. Havass, U.S. Patent 3,148,125 (1964).
506. R. L. Felton, U.S. Patent 3,615,289 (1971).
507. A. J. Gunderman and R. D. Forshay, U.S. Patent 3,819,342 (1974).
508. A. Miller and W. Siegfried, U.S. Patent 3,645,705 (1972).
509. J. D. Avelar, U.S. Patent 3,065,120 (1962).
510. G. A. Jachimowicz, U.S. Patent 3,616,176 (1971).
511. H. S. Akrongold and R. Akrongold, U.S. Patent 3,654,167 (1972).
512. M. M. Renfrew and H. Wittcoff, U.S. Patent 2,705,223 (1955).
513. G. G. Wilson, U.S. Patent 2,839,549 (1958).
514. D. E. Peerman and D. E. Floyd, U.S. Patent 2,881,194 (1959).
515. H. J. Sharkey, U.S. Patent 3,280,140 (1966).
516. D. E. Floyd and D. E. Peerman, U.S. Patent 2,999,825 (1961).
517. O. Ernst, U.S. Patent 3,008,909 (1961).
518. R. Janssen, M. Drawert and E. Griebsch, U.S. Patent 3,563,927 (1971).
519. *Chemical Economics Handbook*, Stanford Research Institute, Menlo Park, California, p. 580.1033T, March, 1974.
520. D. Glaser, U.S. Patent 2,990,383 (1961).
521. S. O. Greenlee, U.S. Patent 2,852,477 (1958).
522. Belgian Patent 691,582 (1967).
523. C. Klomp and G. van Ooosterhoff, Canadian Patent 773,157 (1967).
524. R. Jorda, German Patent 1,251,448 (1967).
525. J. B. Harrison, L. D. Hignett and J. K. Gentles, U.S. Patent 3,352,804 (1967).
526. D. Glaser, U.S. Patent 2,844,552 (1958).
527. H. Zumstein, U.S. Patent 2,977,332 (1961).
528. J. N. S. Kwong, U.S. Patent 3,257,342 (1966).
529. D. E. Peerman, U.S. Patent 3,242,131 (1966).

530. D. E. Peerman and D. E. Floyd, U.S. Patent 2,891,023 (1959).
531. M. Honnen, U.S. Patent 2,930,774 (1960).
532. D. H. Wheeler and D. E. Floyd, U.S. Patent 3,306,865 (1967).
533. J. B. Boylan, U.S. Patent 3,277,034 (1966).
534. G. A. Hudson, U.S. Patent 2,955,513 (1961).
535. E. Griebsch and W. Goetze, German Patent 1,090,803 (1960).
536. R. M. Jorda, U.S. Patent 3,159,499 (1964).
537. British Patent 951,953 (1964).
538. C. E. Workman, U.S. Patent 3,164,488 (1965).
539. D. E. Floyd, U.S. Patent 2,944,036 (1960).
540. D. E. Peerman, U.S. Patent 2,994,456 (1961).
541. L. E. Schniepp, R. E. Mietz and J. H. Groves, U.S. Patent 2,986,539 (1961).
542. British Patent 1,056,899 (1967).
543. H. Jedlicka, British Patent 1,037,989 (1966).
544. F. D. Johnson, U.S. Patent 2,939,805 (1960).
545. E. C. Johnson and R. D. Clarke, U.S. Patent 2,912,398 (1959).
546. T. C. Morris and A. M. Chaplick, U.S. Patent 2,867,592 (1959).
547. W. E. St. Clair and R. H. Moult, U.S. Patent 2,981,702 (1961).
548. D. P. Hart, U.S. Patent 2,919,255 (1959).
549. G. Swann and P. G. Evans, U.S. Patent 2,956,968 (1960).
550. G. W. Schardt, U.S. Patent 2,993,014 (1961).
551. H. Witcoff and M. M. Renfrew, Canadian Patent 544,554 (1957).
552. G. L. Baumgartner, Jr., U.S. Patent 2,904,524 (1959).
553. T. J. Coe, U.S. Patent 2,890,097 (1959); 2,933,366 (1960).
554. C. E. Pardo, Jr. and R. A. O'Connell, U.S. Patent 3,019,076 (1962).
555. C. E. Pardo, Jr. and R. E. Foster, U.S. Patent 3,033,706 (1962).
556. C. H. Binkley and C. E. Pardo, Jr., U.S. Patent 2,933,409 (1960).
557. J. A. Bassett and M. H. Battles, U.S. Patent 3,274,023 (1966).
558. P. C. Cassidy and M. Giella, U.S. Patent 3,220,962 (1965).
559. M. H. Battles, J. A. Bassett, P. C. Cassidy and M. Giella, U.S. Patent 3,130,069 (1964).
560. R. A. O'Connell, U.S. Patent 2,900,291 (1959).
561. G. I. Keim, U.S. Patent 2,926,154 (1960).
562. D. C. Babcock, U.S. Patent 3,224,990 (1965).
563. J. W. Hyland, Jr., U.S. Patent 3,248,280 (1966); 3,434,984 (1969).
564. British Patent 972,801 (1964); Belgian Patent 638,157 (1963).
565. British Patent 1,078,722 (1967).
566. L. F. Schaeffer, Jr. and A. J. Slosser, U.S. Patent 3,265,647 (1966).
567. A. G. Sternberg, U.S. Patent 2,934,452 (1960).
568. S. W. Street, U.S. Patent 3,202,621 (1965).

569. W. C. Simpson and H. J. Sommer, U.S. Patent 3,105,771 (1963).
570. L. R. Vertnik, U.S. Patent 3,217,028 (1965).
571. W. B. Reynolds and S. A. Harrison, U.S. Patent 3,268,493 (1966).
572. H. N. Dunning, J. M. White and H. Wittcoff, U.S. Patent 3,215,625 (1965).
573. L. R. Vertnik, U.S. Patent 3,281,470 (1966).
574. R. Nordgren, L. R. Vertnik and H. Wittcoff, U.S. Patent 3,235,596 (1966).
575. R. Nordgren and H. A. Wittcoff, U.S. Patent 3,371,116 (1968).

Safety, Storage and Handling of Dimer Acids

5

Edward C. Leonard and Kenneth T. Mecklenborg—
Humko Sheffield Chemical, Memphis, Tennessee

A. TOXICOLOGICAL PROPERTIES OF DIMER ACIDS AND RELATED MATERIALS

The acute oral toxicity and the primary skin and acute eye irritative potentials of dimer acids, distilled dimer acids, trimer acids, and monomer acids have been evaluated based on the techniques specified in the *Regulations for the Enforcement of the Federal Hazardous Substances Act* [Title 16, *Code of Federal Regulations,* 1500.40, 1500.41, 1500.42 (henceforth *CFR*)] (1).

The results of this evaluation are shown in Table 13.

TABLE 13

Dimer Acids and Related Products—Toxicity Data

Sample	Oral LD_{50}	Primary Irritation Index	Eye Irritation
trimer acids	>10.0 ml/kg	0	very slight erythema in six rabbits
distilled dimer acids	>21.5 ml/kg	0.50	very slight erythema in four rabbits
monomer acids	>21.5 ml/kg	1.0	very slight erythema in four rabbits
dimer acids	>21.5 ml/kg	0.75	very slight erythema in three rabbits

Table 13 (continued)

Scoring Key—Primary Irritation

Evaluation of Skin Reactions	Value
Erythema and eschar formation:	
No erythema	0
Very slight erythema	1
Well-defined erythema	2
Moderate to severe erythema	3
Severe erythema (beet redness) to slight eschar formation (injuries in depth)	4
Edema formation:	
No edema	0
Very slight edema (barely perceptible)	1
Slight edema (edges of area well-defined by definite raising)	2
Moderate edema (raised approximately one millimeter)	3
Severe edema (raised more than one millimeter and extending beyond the area of exposure)	4

(from paragraph 1500.41 of Title 16, *CFR*)

Based on these results, trimer acids, distilled dimer acids, monomer acids, and dimer acids are classified as non-toxic by ingestion, are not primary skin irritants or corrosive materials, and are not eye irritants as these terms are defined in the Federal regulations.

B. FOOD-ADDITIVE AND FOOD-PACKAGING REGULATIONS

There are no Federal regulations covering *direct* use (food additive) of dimer acids in food products. All of the regulations cited here deal with indirect use in packaging materials, with incidental food contact.

The regulations in which dimer acids are mentioned are the following:

21 CFR 121.2507 dimer acids as a component of polyamide resins for coating cellophane,
21 CFR 121.2514 dimer acids as a component of epoxy, polyester, or polyamide resins for "resinous and polymeric coatings" that come into contact with food,
21 CFR 121.2548 dimer acids as a component of a zinc-silicon dioxide matrix coating which is the food-contact surface of articles intended for use in producing, manufac-

turing, packing, processing, preparing, treating, packaging, transporting, or holding food,

21 CFR 121.2550 dimer acids as components of "resinous and polymeric coatings" used in closures with sealing gaskets for food containers,

21 CFR 121.2557 dimer or trimer acids as defoaming agents in coatings manufacture, with the coatings ultimately destined for food use,

21 CFR 121.2559 dimer acids as components of "resinous and polymeric coatings" used as adjuvants for other resins used in food-contact coatings,

21 CFR 121.2569 dimer acids as a component of polyamide resins used as coatings for food-contact polyolefin films,

21 CFR 121.2571 dimer acids as components of "resinous and polymeric coatings" for paper and paperboard in contact with dry food.

These capsule descriptions of the regulations are abstracted from very detailed (in some instances multi-page) regulations in Title 21 of the *Code of Federal Regulations*. Careful reading of these regulations is recommended for those seriously interested in the subject.

C. FLAMMABILITY

Closed cup flash points have recently been suggested (2) as a criterion of flammability by the United States Department of Transportation. Materials with a closed cup flash point of <100°F would be classed as flammable, those with flash points in the range 100-200°F would be designated combustible, and those with a flash point greater than 200°F would be neither flammable nor combustible. Table 14 shows flash and fire points for dimer acids and related products (3). Dimer acids do not represent a fire hazard, based on these values.

TABLE 14

*Flash and Fire Points of Dimer Acids
and Related Products*

Product	Flash Point (°F)		Fire Point (°F)
	Open Cup	*Closed Cup*	*Open Cup*
Monomer acids	380	310	420
Dimer acids	535	475	605
Trimer acids	625	570	655

D. STORAGE AND HANDLING OF DIMER ACIDS AND RELATED PRODUCTS

Since dimer acids, monomer acids, and trimer acids are unsaturated fatty acids, they are susceptible to oxidative and thermal attack, and will corrode metals. Special precautions are necessary, therefore, to prevent product color development and equipment deterioration.

1. Storage

Type 304 stainless steel is recommended for storage tanks for dimer acids. Aluminum (Alloy 3003) and reinforced plastics have also been suggested for the same purpose. Aluminum, however, presents the risk of damage from alkaline cleaning solutions, and reinforced-plastic construction suffers from temperature limitations. For heating coils (4) and for agitators 316-stainless is preferred (heating coils approximately 50 square feet of heat transfer surface in the form of a 2-inch schedule-10 U-bend scroll are recommended for a 10,000-gallon tank).

It is recommended that dimer acids storage tanks have an inert-gas blanket, preferably nitrogen. A closed-vent system is used with a slight positive pressure. This can effectively be accomplished with a conservation vent which operates at a 5″ water-column pressure setting and a 1″ water-column vacuum-relief setting with the inert-gas blanket pressure setting of ~2-3″ water column. As the tank is being filled, the incoming liquid displaces the inert gas, relieving at 5″ water-column internal pressure. Conversely, as the material is removed from the tank, the pressure drops below the inert-gas regulator set pressure and the inert gas is thus allowed to displace the liquid being pumped from the tank. In case the inert gas is shut off while liquid is being removed from the tank, the vacuum relief will protect the tank by admitting outside air.

Tank instrumentation should include devices to measure temperature, pressure, and stock level. Manholes should be provided to facilitate cleaning and maintenance. Sample cocks are also obvious necessities.

A preferred tank insulation is foamglass block. This is normally enclosed with corrugated aluminum held firmly with bands.

Centrifugal pumps may be used to transfer dimer acids stock. 316-stainless-steel pump construction (for surfaces in contact with the organic material) is recommended. Pipe, valves and fittings may be of 304-stainless if the liquid temperature is maintained below 225°F. Above 225°F, 316-ss provides better corrosion resistance. All lines should be traced electrically or with steam to maintain a flowing temperature as listed below. Due to the high viscosities, care must be taken to size all lines properly.

2. Handling

The recommended temperature ranges for transfer of dimer acids and related stocks are shown in Table 15. Specific gravities and viscosities for these chemicals, in the recommended temperature ranges for transfer, are shown in Table 16.

TABLE 15

Pumping-Temperature Ranges for Dimer Acids Stocks

Stock	Pumping-Temperature Range (°F).
Dimer acids	130-170 (160 optimum)
Monomer acids	115-120
Trimer acids	170-180

TABLE 16

DIMER ACIDS STOCKS

Specific Gravities and Viscosities at Pumping Temperatures

	Temperature (°F)	Specific Gravity (t/25°C)	Viscosity (cSt @t)
Monomer acids	120	0.890	23
Dimer acids	160	0.923	305
Trimer acids	175	0.926	669

The temperature should never exceed 180°F. Even with an inert-gas blanket, color deterioration of the products accelerates at higher temperatures. Dimer and trimer acids stored for any lengthy time period should be held at approximately 120°F. Tank agitators should be interlocked with the steam coils so that whenever the stream is on the agitator will be moving the liquid to prevent local discoloration of the stock in the vicinity of the coils.

Stainless-steel or epoxy-lined tank cars and tank trucks are recommended for shipping. Aluminum has also been used. The tank can be flushed with carbon dioxide before loading, and blanketed with nitrogen after loading. Drum shipments are recommended in epoxy-lined open-head drums fitted with a bung. Dimer acids and its by-products contaminated with iron or copper show accelerated color deterioration. Exposure to these metals, or their salts, should be minimized.

REFERENCES FOR CHAPTER FIVE

1. The Federal Hazardous Substances Act is the legal definition of certain safety criteria for chemicals which are *consumer* products. Dimer acids and associated'products are industrial rather than consumer products, so that the evaluation reported here simply represents product property information, rather than legally significant data, at this time.
2. Amendments 172.23, 173.78, 174.19 and 177.29 to 49*CFR* 172, 49*CFR* 173, 49*CFR* 174, and 49*CFR* 177 published in the *Federal Register,* Volume 39, Number 17, pp. 2766, 2769, 2770, 2771 and 2772, Thursday, January 24, 1974. Closed cup flash points and ranges will be mandatory criteria for flammability determination after July 1, 1975.
3. The values reported here have been determined on batches of dimer products produced in 1974 by Humko Sheffield Chemical.
4. Bulletin Number 419C, Organic Chemicals Division, Emery Industries, Inc., February, 1972.

INDEX